MATHS GAMES

FOR LESS ABLE LEARNERS

AGES 7 TO 11

WENDY SINGLETON

Author	Editor	Assistant Editor
Wendy Singleton	**Helen Skelton**	**Aileen Lalor**

Series Designer	Designer	Cover
Anna Oliwa	**Micky Pledge**	**Martyn Chillmaid**

Illustrator

Jim Peacock

Text © 2004 Wendy Singleton
© 2004 Scholastic Ltd

Designed using Adobe InDesign

Published by Scholastic Ltd, Villiers House, Clarendon Avenue,
Leamington Spa, Warwickshire CV32 5PR

www.scholastic.co.uk

Printed by Bell and Bain Ltd, Glasgow

1 2 3 4 5 6 7 8 9 0   4 5 6 7 8 9 0 1 2 3

British Library Cataloguing-in-Publication Data
A catalogue record for this book is available from the British Library.

ISBN 0439-98456-4

CONTENTS

INTRODUCTION

Why a book of games for less able learners?

This book has been written for teachers, teaching assistants and all those working with Key Stage 2 children in single or mixed-age groups in mixed ability classes attending mainstream schools.

The purpose of the book is to give you a selection of games, linked to learning objectives from the National Numeracy Strategy's (NNS) *Framework for Teaching Mathematics* and the NNS Unit Plans, that are accessible to less able learners. (Information about the NNS Unit Plans, including how to acquire them, is given at the end of this introduction.)

For the purposes of this book the term 'less able learners' refers to any children who are working below the level expected of their chronological age, but who should nevertheless be included in all parts of the daily mathematics lesson – DfES guidance is very clear about this.

While it is wholly appropriate in some contexts to make activities accessible to the less able simply by changing the range of numbers/operations involved, there are many occasions when this is not appropriate – nor indeed possible. The games in this book offer some additional approaches. One of these approaches is 'tracking back'. This is the process of looking for parallel or supporting objectives from lower year groups, which the less able can work on at their own level while remaining in step with the rest of the class.

In general terms, the year group objectives covered in this book have been tracked back and the games have been pitched for a level of ability two years below that expected for the chronological age of the group.

The objectives have then been tracked forward and the games differentiated according to those objectives for the two intervening year groups. Differentiation is achieved using different versions of the same game. This approach allows all (or most) children in the class to be involved in the same basic activity, regardless of ability or age, thus minimising the planning and preparation time.

It also, or alternatively, offers a clear progression for less able learners who may well start by playing the version of the game aimed at the level of two

years below their chronological age and then move through to the version of the game which is pitched at the level of understanding expected for their actual chronological age. Because each game is differentiated in this way, children can progress at their own rate in each aspect of mathematics represented.

Using these games to support less able learners provides motivation and interest and allows for variety in both teaching and learning styles, essential if the different needs of these children are to be met.

How are the games organised?

The games in this book are organised into four year group sections that reflect the year group the children playing the games will be in (that is, according to their actual age): Year 3 to Year 6. Each section contains nine games, three for each term of the school year.

For each year group, the games address objectives from three strands of the NNS Framework for that year:
● Numbers and the number system (with a slight bias towards this strand in the earlier year groups and a focus on fractions and decimals in the later age groups)
● Calculations (with the main emphasis throughout on mental calculation strategies)
● Measures, shape and space (including time and money).

Each game has a page of teaching notes and at least one photocopiable resource page.

The teaching notes outline the objectives being addressed and supported by the game, other resources required or that could be used to set the game in context, and some support on your teaching input to help the children get the most out of the game. The notes detail 'How to play' and the variations that will make the game more challenging as the children progress towards the level at which the rest of the class is working.

Which objectives are covered?

At the beginning of the book there are 4 grids setting out the objectives for each game, one grid for each year group. The grids relate each game to a unit in the NNS Unit Plan for that year (for those teachers who make use of them) and to the relevant objective for that year group (which can be found in both the *Framework for Teaching Mathematics* and the Unit Plan). This objective is then tracked back across two years, through the Framework's 'Yearly teaching programmes', to link with the parallel and/or underpinning objectives in the prior years.

There are two objectives described in the notes for each game:
● The 'Game objectives' which are taken from the yearly teaching programme two years below the chronological age group
● The chronological age group's objectives that the rest of the class will be working towards.

At the end of each game, there is a clear indication of how the game can be differentiated and developed across the different age groups' objectives to track back up to arrive at the chronological age group's objectives.

The grids, the stated game objectives and the 'progression' information to support differentiation give comprehensive objective coverage across three age/ability groups for each game.

How should the photocopiable pages be used?

Each game has photocopiable resources designed specifically to support the playing of the game. Many of them are score sheets or recording sheets. Some are pieces with which to play the game and some are game boards. Before making use of the photocopiable pages several points should be considered:

● Some of the photocopiable pages would be better enlarged to A3 before use, either to make the playing pieces a more manageable size or to make spaces on a game board large enough for counters.

● The life of photocopiable game boards and playing pieces can be prolonged by laminating (or covering with clear, sticky-backed plastic).

● All photocopiable resources can be made more attractive to children, and therefore more motivating, if they are copied on to coloured card.

● Pages intended to be used as scoring or recording sheets would benefit from being laminated (or covered with clear, sticky-backed plastic). In this way, they can be used again and again to 'write on–wipe off'.

What other resources are needed?

The majority of the games need only the resources provided in this book plus some everyday classroom items such as:

● assorted dice – six-sided 'spotty' dice, six-sided numeral dice, ten-sided dice, twenty-sided dice, blank dice with a sheet of self-adhesive spots to put numbers/symbols onto the dice

● dominoes (double 6 sets)

● number lines of various sizes, including those showing negative numbers

● hundred squares

● counting sticks

● digit cards

● Counting objects (counters, plastic dinosaurs, animals, people and so on)

● 3-D and 2-D shapes

● interlocking cubes

● coins (real, if possible)

● calculators

● weights and weighing scales

● rulers

● arrow/partitioning cards.

Details of suggested suppliers for general classroom resources can be found at the end of the Introduction.

How are the NNS Interactive Teaching Programs (ITPs) used?

The NNS Interactive Teaching Programs are an extremely valuable ICT aid to teaching and learning. They are intended primarily as a teaching and demonstration aid for use by the teacher and are sophisticated and flexible extensions to the kind of resources in common use in the Daily Maths Lesson (number lines, counting sticks, hundred squares and so on).

The 'Number grid' program, for example, can be used to highlight all the multiples of, say, 3 or 5 on a hundred square. The 'Tell the time' program allows the manipulation of the hands on an analogue clock and will either simultaneously or separately show the corresponding digital display. The 'Fractions' program can be used in exactly the same way as a fractions strip but can be manipulated on screen to meet the needs of both teacher and children.

You will find that selected ITPs have been suggested as resources to support your teaching around the games. You may like to use them during your teaching input to the whole class or in a small group demonstration to further reinforce the maths being practised. In the text accompanying the games, where an ITP is listed, no direct instruction is given as to how, where and when to use the programs. If you are familiar with the ITPs and have access to this resource in your classroom, make use of them in whatever way you prefer to enhance the learning. Less able children often respond very favourably to ICT resources. However, in the context of this book, it is not appropriate for the children to use the ITPs when playing the games. If you are not familiar with the programs, you will need to acquire them and explore their potential before using them. They can be downloaded free of charge from the DfES website (for the address see the 'Useful information' section below).

How can adult help support these games?

When working with children, and particularly with less able learners, these things play a vital role in the development of mathematical understanding:
● the use of effective questioning
● the correct use of language and vocabulary
● discussion, explanation and reasoning.

It is in these areas that an adult's involvement can make the most significant contribution to the child's learning through games. The adult has two main areas of involvement:

The teaching input suggested for each game requires the teacher or teaching assistant to:
● revise and discuss the skills, knowledge and understanding needed to play the game, using demonstration and teaching tools such as number lines, fraction strips or ITPs
● introduce and/or reinforce the correct and appropriate vocabulary
● explain and demonstrate the use of game boards and pieces and ensure that children understand the rules of play.

During the game an adult should listen and observe, only intervening to:
● draw out the intended learning or consolidation the game offers
● ensure that the rules are being followed correctly
● deal with any misconceptions that may be developing
● relate the game to other areas of learning and experience

- encourage those children who lack confidence
- prevent the game being dominated by one child to the detriment of others.

There is an optional feedback sheet provided as a photocopiable page on page 96 for use by teaching assistants working with the children who are playing the games. This sheet can form the basis of communication between teacher and teaching assistant and/or as a record of children's achievements/difficulties.

Useful information

National Numeracy Strategy Unit Plans for Years 4, 5 and 6 (complete coverage) and for Years 1, 2 and 3 (selected units only) can be obtained free of charge via the DfES website,
www.standards.dfes.gov.uk/numeracy/publications.

The NNS Interactive Teaching Programs (or ITPs) can also be downloaded free of charge from the DfES website.

Suggested suppliers of basic classroom equipment

TTS Active Maths
Nunn Brook Rd
Huthwaite
Sutton-in-Ashfield
Nottinghamshire
NG17 2HU
Tel: 0800 31868
Email: sales@tts-group.co.uk
Website: www.tts-group.co.uk

Hope Education
Hyde Buildings
Ashton Rd
Hyde
Cheshire
SK14 4SH
Tel: 08451 202055
Email: orders@hope-education.co.uk
Website: hope-education.co.uk

YEAR 3 OBJECTIVES

Game	Unit Plan	Year 3 objective (From Unit Plan)	Parallel Year 2 objective (From Framework yearly teaching programme)	Year 1 objective (From Framework yearly teaching programme)
1. Which way? (page 13)	Autumn term Unit 2	Continue to recognise that addition can be done in any order. Put the largest number first and count on.	Put the largest number first and count on in tens and ones.	Begin to recognise that addition can be done in any order. Begin to recognise that more than two numbers can be added together.
2. All change (page 16)	Autumn term Unit 3	Understand and use £.p notation. Solve word problems involving money, including finding totals, giving change, and working out which coins to pay.	Recognise all coins and begin to use £.p notation for money. Find totals, give change and work out which coins to pay.	Recognise coins of different values. Find totals and change from up to 20p. Work out how to pay an exact sum using smaller coins.
3. Add and add again (page 18)	Autumn term Unit 9	Understand multiplication as repeated addition.	Understand the operation of multiplication as repeated addition.	Count in steps of 5 from zero to 20 or more; begin to count on in steps of 3 from zero. Begin to recognise that more than two numbers can be added together.
4. Three to win (page 20)	Spring term Unit 2	Extend understanding that more than two numbers can be added. Add three or four single-digit numbers mentally.	Understand that more than two numbers can be added. Begin to add three single-digit numbers mentally (totals up to about 20).	Begin to recognise that more than two numbers can be added together.
5. Count on (page 22)	Spring term Unit 8	Count on or back in tens or hundreds, starting from any two- or three-digit number.	Count on or back in ones or tens, starting from any two-digit number.	Count on and back in ones from any small number and in tens from and back to zero.
6. What next? (page 24)	Spring term Unit 8	Solve mathematical problems or puzzles, recognise simple patterns and relationships, generalise and predict.	Solve mathematical problems or puzzles; recognise simple patterns and relationships, generalise and predict.	Solve simple mathematical problems or puzzles; recognise and predict from simple patterns and relationships.
7. Your money or mine? (page 26)	Spring term Unit 9	Solve word problems involving money, including finding totals, giving change, and working out which coins to pay.	Use mental addition and subtraction to solve simple word problems involving money.	Use mental strategies to solve simple problems set in real life money or measurement contexts. Recognise coins of different values. Find totals and change from up to 20p. Work out how to pay an exact sum using smaller coins.
8. Does it go? (page 28)	Summer term Unit 8	Recognise two-digit and three-digit multiples of 2, 5 or 10 and three digit multiples of 50 and 100.	Begin to recognise two-digit multiples of 2, 5 or 10.	Begin to recognise odd and even numbers to about 20 as every other number.
9. What's it got? (page 30)	Summer term Unit 8	Recognise two-digit and three-digit multiples of 2, 5 or 10 and three digit multiples of 50 and 100.	Begin to recognise two-digit multiples of 2, 5 or 10.	Begin to recognise odd and even numbers to about 20 as every other number.

YEAR 4 OBJECTIVES

Game	Unit Plan	Year 3 objective (From Unit Plan)	Parallel Year 2 objective (From Framework yearly teaching programme)	Year 1 objective (From Framework yearly teaching programme)
10. Shape match (page 32)	Autumn term Unit 4	Classify polygons using criteria such as number of right angles, whether or not they are regular, symmetry properties.	Classify and describe 3-D and 2-D shapes, referring to properties such as reflective symmetry and other properties.	Sort shapes and describe some of their features, such as the number of sides and corners, symmetry and other properties.
11. Odds and evens (page 34)	Autumn term Unit 8	Recognise odd and even numbers up to 1000 and some of their properties, including the outcome of sums or differences in pairs of odd/ even numbers.	Count on and back in twos, starting from any two-digit number, and recognise odd and even numbers to at least 100.	Count on in twos from and back to zero or any small number, and recognise odd and even numbers to at least 30.
12. Doubles and halves (page 36)	Autumn term Unit 9	Use doubling or halving starting from known facts.	Use doubling or halving, starting from known facts.	Know by heart the doubles of all numbers to ten and the corresponding halves. Derive quickly doubles of all numbers to at least 15.
13. Mass matters (page 42)	Spring term Unit 4	Record estimates and readings from scales to a suitable degree of accuracy.	Read scales to the nearest division. Record estimates and measurements to the nearest whole or half unit.	Estimate, measure and compare masses, using standard units. Read a simple scale to the nearest labelled division.
14. Five to win (page 44)	Spring term Unit 8	Recognise and extend number sequences formed by counting from any number in steps of constant size, extending beyond zero when counting back.	Describe and extend number sequences; count on or back in tens or hundreds, starting from any two- or three-digit number.	Describe and extend simple number sequences; count on or back in ones or tens, starting from any two-digit number.
15. Tables test (page 46)	Spring term Unit 9	Know by heart multiplication facts for 2, 3, 4, 5 and 10 times-tables.	Know by heart multiplication facts for 2, 5 and 10 times-tables.	Know by heart multiplication facts for 2 and 10 times-tables.
16. Ups and downs (page 48)	Summer term Unit 1	Round any positive integer less than 1000 to the nearest 10 or 100.	Round any two-digit number to the nearest 10 and any three-digit number to the nearest 100.	Round numbers less than 100 to the nearest 10.
17. Take two (page 50)	Summer term Unit 2	Use known number facts and place value, to add or subtract mentally, including any pair of two-digit whole numbers.	Add and subtract mentally a 'near multiple of 10' to or from a two-digit number by adding or subtracting 10, 20, 30… and adjusting.	Add/subtract 9 or 11: add/subtract 10 and adjust by 1. Begin to add/ subtract 19 or 21: add/subtract 20 and adjust by 1.
18. Snakes and arrows (page 52)	Summer term Unit 4	Suggest suitable units and measuring equipment to estimate or measure length, mass or capacity. Record estimates and readings from scales to a suitable degree of accuracy.	Suggest suitable units and measuring equipment to estimate or measure length, mass or capacity. Record estimates and measurements to the nearest whole or half unit, (eg 'about 3.5kg').	Estimate, measure and compare lengths, masses and capacities, using standard units.

YEAR 5 OBJECTIVES

Game	Unit Plan	Year 3 objective (From Unit Plan)	Parallel Year 2 objective (From Framework yearly teaching programme)	Year 1 objective (From Framework yearly teaching programme)
19 Shoot the digits (page 57)	Autumn term Unit 1	Read and write whole numbers in figures and words, and know what each digit represents.	Read and write whole numbers to at least 10 000 in figures and words, and know what each digit represents.	Read and write whole numbers to at least 1000 in figures and words, and know what each digit represents.
20 Hexed (page 59)	Autumn term Unit 3	Estimate by approximating (round to nearest 10 or 100), then check result.	Estimate and check by approximating (round to nearest 10 or 100).	Round any two-digit number to the nearest 10 and any three-digit number to the nearest 100.
21 All the fours (page 62)	Autumn term Unit 8	Recognise properties of rectangles. Classify triangles (isosceles, equilateral, scalene) using criteria such as equal sides, equal angles lines of symmetry.	Recognise equilateral and isosceles triangles. Classify polygons using criteria such as number of right angles, whether or not they are regular, symmetry properties.	Classify and describe 3-D and 2-D shapes, including quadrilaterals.
22 More or less? (page 64)	Spring term Unit 1	Use the vocabulary of comparing and ordering numbers, including symbols such as <, >, ≤, ≥ and =.	Read and write the vocabulary of comparing and ordering numbers. Use symbols correctly, including less than (<), greater than (>) and equals (=).	Read and begin to write the vocabulary of comparing and ordering numbers.
23 Factory (page 66)	Spring term Unit 3	Use factors (eg 8 x 12 = 8 x 4 x 3).	Use closely related facts (eg develop the 6x from the 4x and 2x tables).	Understand multiplication as repeated addition.
24 Crazy cubes (page 68)	Spring term Unit 5a	Visualise 3-D shapes from 2-D drawings.	Visualise 3-D shapes from 2-D drawings and identify simple nets of solid shapes.	Make and describe shapes and patterns: for example, explore the different shapes that can be made from four cubes.
25 What's left? (page 70)	Summer term Unit 2	Begin to express a quotient as a fraction or decimal when dividing a whole number by 2, 4, 5 or 10. Round up or down after division, depending on the context.	Find remainders after division.	Begin to find remainders after simple division.
26 Fraction race (page 72)	Summer term Unit 4	Relate fractions to their decimal representation: that is, recognise the equivalence between the decimal and fraction forms of one half, one quarter, three quarters and tenths and hundredths.	Recognise the equivalence between the decimal and fraction forms of one half and one quarter, and tenths such as 0.3.	Begin to recognise simple equivalent fractions: for example, five tenths and one half, five fifths and one whole.
27 What's the time? (page 75)	Summer term Unit 10	Use units of time; read the time on a 24-hour digital clock and use 24-hour clock notation such as 19:53.	Read the time from an analogue clock to the nearest minute, and from a 12-hour digital clock. Use am and pm and the notation 9:53.	Read the time to five minutes on an analogue clock and a 12-hour digital clock, and use the notation 9:40.

YEAR 6 OBJECTIVES

Game	Unit Plan	Year 3 objective (From Unit Plan)	Parallel Year 2 objective (From Framework yearly teaching programme)	Year 1 objective (From Framework yearly teaching programme)
28 Calculating points (page 78)	Autumn term Unit 1	Multiply and divide decimals by 10 or 100 and integers by 1000, and explain the effect.	Multiply and divide any positive integer up to 10 000 by 10 or 100 and understand the effect.	Multiply or divide any integer up to 1000 by 10 (whole-number answers), and understand the effect. Begin to multiply by 100.
29 Left-overs (page 80)	Autumn term Unit 3	Use informal pencil and paper methods to support, record or explain multiplications and divisions.	Extend written methods to short division of HTU by U.	Use informal pencil and paper methods to support, record or explain multiplications and divisions. Develop and refine written methods for TU ÷ U.
30 Let's co-ordinate! (page 82)	Autumn term Unit 10	Read and plot co-ordinates in all four quadrants.	Read and plot co-ordinates in the first quadrant.	Describe and find the position of a point on a grid of squares where the lines are numbered. Recognise simple examples of horizontal and vertical lines.
31 To zero and beyond (page 84)	Spring term Unit 1	Find the difference between a positive and negative integer, or two negative integers, in a context such as temperature or a number line, and order a set of positive and negative integers.	Order a given set of positive and negative integers. Calculate a temperature rise or fall across 0°C.	Recognise negative numbers in context (eg on a number line, on a temperature scale).
32 Decimal dominoes (page 86)	Spring term Unit 7	Use known number facts and place value to consolidate mental addition/subtraction.	Use informal pencil and paper methods to support, record or explain additions and subtractions.	Understand decimal notation and place value for tenths and hundredths, and use it in context.
33 Measure for measure (page 88)	Spring term Unit 9	Use, read and write standard metric units of length, mass and capacity (km, m, cm, mm, kg, g, l, ml, cl), including their abbreviations, and relationships between them.	Use, read and write standard metric units (km, m, cm, mm, kg, g, l, ml), including their abbreviations, and relationships between them.	Use, read and write standard metric units (km, m, cm, mm, kg, g, l, ml), including their abbreviations. Know and use the relationships between familiar units of length, mass and capacity.
34 Money in its place (page 90)	Summer term Unit 1	Order a mixed set of numbers with up to three decimal places.	Order a set of numbers or measurements with the same number of decimal places.	Understand decimal notation and place value for tenths and hundredths and use it in context, for example, order amounts of money.
35 Exactly right (page 92)	Summer term Unit 2	Derive quickly division facts corresponding to tables up to 10 x 10.	Derive quickly, or continue to derive quickly division facts corresponding to tables up to 10 x 10.	Derive quickly division facts corresponding to 2, 3, 4, 5 and 10 times-tables.
36 Lines and angles (page 94)	Summer term Unit 3	Classify quadrilaterals using criteria such as parallel sides, equal angles, equal sides.	Recognise properties of rectangles. Classify triangles using criteria such as equal sides, equal angles, lines of symmetry.	Recognise equilateral and isosceles triangles. Classify polygons using criteria such as number of right angles, whether or not they are regular, symmetry properties.

1. Which way?

Teaching input

There should be some initial discussion about addition strategies, including the fact that addition can be done in any order and that more than two numbers can be added together. The game can then be played with or without objects to count, depending on the needs of the children involved. If objects are an appropriate tool, they should be interesting and motivating, for example, plastic dinosaurs.

During the game, the adult working with the children should be helping them to develop their understanding of addition:

● that it is more efficient to start with the larger/largest number

● that when three numbers are to be added together, there is often a more efficient order for the addition than the one in which they appear (3 + 6 + 7 for example, is best done as 3 + 7 + 6).

Grouping
Small group with adult

Resources
● A set of digit cards 1–9 (use 1–9 cards from photocopiable page 14)
● Objects to count (optional)
● Counters for scoring

Vocabulary
add
total
altogether
score

HOW TO PLAY

1 In turn, players shuffle the digit cards and place them face down in a pile (they must be shuffled every time play passes to another player).

2 The player takes the top three cards and places them face up on the table (in the early stages of addition practice the players may take just two cards).

3 With adult help if necessary, the player uses known strategies to total the two/three numbers. The other players add the numbers in a different order or using a different strategy, to check the answer given.

4 If it is agreed that the answer given is correct, the player takes two counters as his/her 'score'.

5 Appropriate adult intervention should be used discreetly to ensure that no child ends the game with a zero 'score'.

6 The winner is the first player to collect 10 counters (other rules to decide the winner can be devised as necessary).

Progression towards the Year 3 objective

● Use two sets of digit cards 1–9. Players make a two-digit and a one-digit number from the three drawn.

● Play 'Tickets please' (you will need photocopiable page 15 cut up into individual 'tickets'):

1 Shuffle the tickets and place them face down in a pile.

2 In turn, players draw two tickets, arrange them with the larger number first and add the numbers together, recording their total (the other players check the calculation by adding the numbers in a different order or using a different strategy).

3 When each player has had a turn, the one with the highest/lowest total wins that round (alternatively a scoring system as described above can be used).

● All of these variations need an adult present to discuss the strategies being developed and practised.

NNS FRAMEWORK OBJECTIVES

Game objectives
● Begin to recognise that addition can be done in any order.
● Begin to recognise that more than two numbers can be added together.

Year 3 objectives
● Continue to recognise that addition can be done in any order.
● Put the largest number first and count on.

Links to Unit Plan
Year 3 Autumn term
Unit 2 Money, addition and subtraction

Which way? (1)

4	3	2	1	0
9	8	7	6	5

Which way? (2)

(cards for the game 'Tickets please')

16	19	24	8
5	14	27	11
21	7	4	17
13	25	9	23
22	18	6	12
26	29	15	28

2. All change

Grouping
Pairs

Resources
● One standard dice
● A small amount of 1p, 2p, 5p and 10p coins
● Game board (Photocopiable page 17)

Vocabulary
coin
penny
pence
change
how much
amount
worth

Teaching input

This game can be played at various levels. At its most basic, it will use penny coins and 10p coins only with the intention of reinforcing the idea of exchange (for example that ten penny coins have the same value as one ten pence coin). As children's understanding develops, other coins can be introduced, one at a time, until the game is being played with 1p, 2p, 5p and 10p coins. The version described here uses all of these coins. In preparation for the game, at whatever level, the children should have some discussion and practice in exchanging lower value coins for higher value coins and vice versa.

HOW TO PLAY

1 In turn players roll the dice and place on the 'plate', the amount of money represented by the number on the dice, in any combination of coins, for example, a dice roll of 6 could be collected as 6 x 1p coins, 3 x 2p coins, 1 x 5p + 1 x 1p coins, or any combination of these.

2 Each time a player makes up the amount of money on the plate to 10p or more, s/he exchanges the coins for one 10p coin (leaving any coins over and above 10p on the plate) and places the 10p in their 'purse'.

3 Play continues in this way and the winner is the first player to have three 10p coins in their purse.

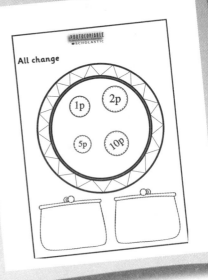

NNS FRAMEWORK OBJECTIVES

Game objectives
● Recognise coins of different values.
● Find totals and change from up to 20p.
● Work out how to pay an exact sum using smaller coins.

Year 3 objectives
● Understand and use £.p notation.
● Solve word problems involving money, including finding totals, giving change and working out which coins to pay.

Links to Unit Plan
Year 3 Autumn term
Unit 3 Money and 'real' life problems

Progression towards the Year 3 objective

● Increase the exchange total to 20p, include 20p coins, and the winner is then the first person to have £1 in their purse.

● Increase the exchange total to £1, include 50p coins, use two ten-sided dice, and the winner is the first person to have £5 in their purse.

● When appropriate, the children should be introduced to the idea of 'paying' the amount represented by the dice by giving too much and receiving change (for example, if the dice show 2 and 9, this could be 29p or 92p, and could be paid as one 20p coin and one 10p coin, the player taking 1p from the plate, or as a £1 coin, the player taking 8p change from the plate).

● At a stage appropriate to needs, players should record, at the beginning or end of their turn, the amount of money on the plate, in order to practise and consolidate the use of £.p notation.

All change

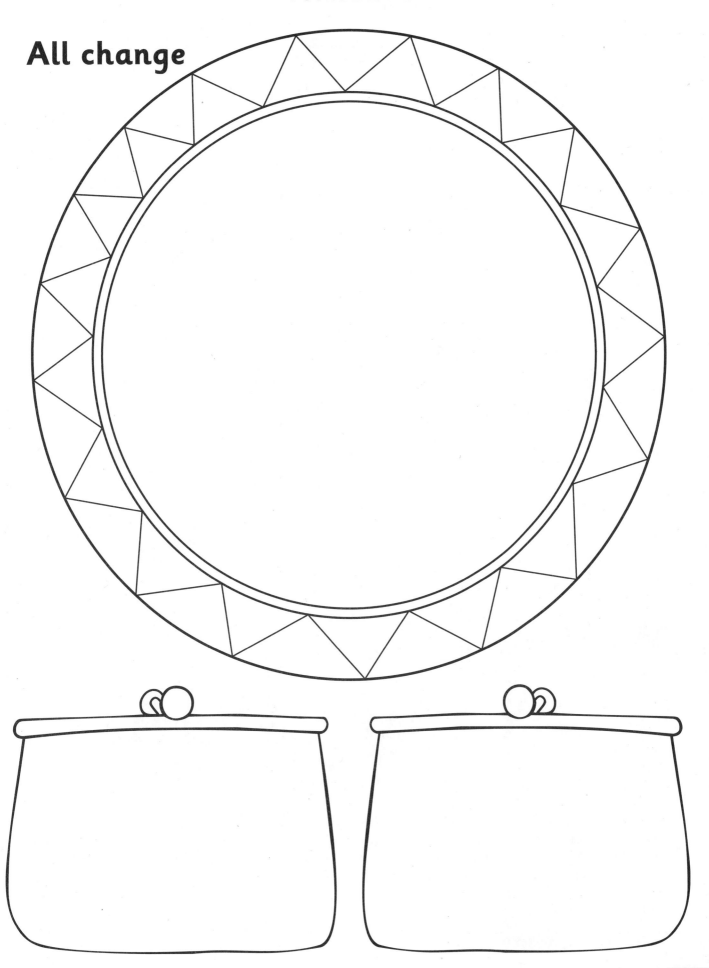

3. Add and add again

Grouping
Groups of up to 4 children

Resources
● One standard dice
● A set of cards (made from photocopiable page 19 enlarged to A3)
● 30 counters for counting
● Counters of a different colour (or other objects such as plastic counting toys) for scoring
● Interactive Teaching Program 'Grouping' (optional)

Vocabulary
lots of
groups of
repeated addition
once, twice, three times up to ten times

NNS FRAMEWORK OBJECTIVES

Game objectives
● Count in steps of 5 from zero to 20 or more; begin to count on in steps of 3 from zero.
● Begin to recognise that more that two numbers can be added together.

Year 3 objective
Understand multiplication as repeated addition.

Links to Unit Plan
Year 3 Autumn term
Unit 9 Multiplication and division

Teaching input

In preparation for this game, children need to know and practise how to record a repeated addition as a multiplication. For example: 3 + 3 + 3 + 3 = 12 can also be recorded as 4 x 3 = 12.

HOW TO PLAY

Part 1
Using set of cards A from the photocopiable and a dice, play as follows:
1 Shuffle the set of cards and place them face down in a pile.
2 In turn, players take the top card from the pile and roll the dice.
3 The card tells the player whether to make groups of 2, 3 or 5 counters and the dice roll tells the player how many groups to make.
4 The player makes the groups accordingly with counters and arrives at a total (this may be by counting on in twos, threes, or fives, or by counting the counters individually, depending on the needs and abilities of the children). The total is recorded.
5 When all players have had their turn the person who had the greatest total scores one point and takes a 'scoring' counter/toy. (If two or more players had the same total, each would take a counter.)
6 Play continues in this way until all the cards have been used.
7 The winner is the player with the most 'scoring' counters/toys.

Part 2
Played in exactly the same way but using set of cards B and in each turn the player records their total as both an addition and a multiplication (60 counters will be needed for grouping).

Progression towards the Year 3 objective

Use two ten-sided dice (zero counts as 10 – placing a sticker showing 10 over the zero would make this clear) to generate a multiplication which can be read either way:
● A 6 and a 4, for example, can be read as 4 x 6 or 6 x 4 and should be recorded both ways and as an addition and a multiplication.
● The method of play and scoring is the same as above.

Add and add again

Set A

Groups of 2	Groups of 2	Groups of 2	Groups of 2	Groups of 2
Groups of 3	Groups of 3	Groups of 3	Groups of 3	Groups of 3
Groups of 5	Groups of 5	Groups of 5	Groups of 5	Groups of 5

Set B

Groups of 2	Groups of 3	Groups of 4	Groups of 5	Groups of 10
Groups of 2	Groups of 3	Groups of 4	Groups of 5	Groups of 10
Groups of 2	Groups of 3	Groups of 4	Groups of 5	Groups of 10
Groups of 2	Groups of 3	Groups of 4	Groups of 5	Groups of 10

4. Three to win

Grouping
Pairs

Resources
● Number grid (photocopiable page 21)
● Counters for scoring

Vocabulary
add
total
altogether
more
score

Teaching input
Children should have some practice in using effective strategies for adding together two or three small numbers. The emphasis should be on adding three numbers and deciding on the best order in which to add them. For example:

7 + 1 + 5 might best be done as

5 + 1 = 6 then use a near double to do

6 + 7 = 13 (double 6 plus 1).

HOW TO PLAY

1 Player 1 chooses any three touching numbers and totals them.
2 Player 2 does the same, but may not choose the same three numbers (although up to any two of the three may be chosen).
3 The player whose total was higher is the winner of that round and collects a counter.
4 Play continues until one player has collected 5 counters to win the game.

Note: The following arrangements (or rotations/reflections of these) qualify as three connecting numbers.

NNS FRAMEWORK OBJECTIVES

Game objective
● Begin to recognise that more than two numbers can be added together.

Year 3 objectives
● Extend understanding that more than two numbers can be added.
● Add three or four single-digit numbers mentally.

Links to Unit Plan
Year 3 Spring term
Unit 2 Addition and subtraction

Progression towards the Year 3 objective
● Players choose four touching numbers.
● Make a new grid with some two-digit numbers included and play with first three, then four touching numbers.

Three to win

3	1	8	5	4
8	5	3	1	6
6	4	7	8	3
1	9	1	5	2
4	2	7	6	1
7	9	9	2	9

5. Count on

Grouping
Pairs

Resources
● One dice marked 1, 1, 1, 10, 10, 10
● One standard dice
● A set of digit cards 0 to 9 (photocopiable page 14)
● Two zero to 100 table top number lines (photocopiable page 23)
● Interactive Teaching Program 'Counting On and Back' (optional)

Vocabulary
count on
count back
ones
tens
hundreds

Teaching input

Before playing the game it is useful to do some oral and mental practice of counting on and back in tens and ones from a variety of start numbers. A number line should be used both as a supporting resource and to demonstrate how a count can be recorded.

HOW TO PLAY

1 Before the game starts, the digit cards are shuffled and each player draws one to give them their individual starting number. This is marked on the player's own number line.

2 In turn, players roll the dice marked with ones and tens, and the standard dice. This tells them their move. For example a roll of 5 on the standard dice and 10 on the 'ten and one' dice represents a move of 5 tens (50).

3 Starting at their start number, the player moves along their own number line accordingly and marks the new position.

4 Play continues in this way until one player reaches or passes 100. This person is the winner.

NNS FRAMEWORK OBJECTIVES

Game objective
● Count on and back in ones from any small number and in tens from and back to zero.

Year 3 objective
● Count on or back in tens or hundreds, starting from any two- or three-digit number.

Links to Unit Plan
Year 3 Spring term
Unit 8 Counting, properties of numbers and reasoning about numbers

Progression towards the Year 3 objective

Using a dice marked with 10, 10, 10, 100, 100, 100 and two ten-sided dice, play proceeds as above with the following modifications:

1 In turn, players roll the two ten-sided dice to determine their start number (they use the larger of the two possible numbers: a 5 and a 7 represent 75 not 57).

2 Each player then rolls the dice marked with tens and hundreds and a standard dice to give them their move (100 and 4 represents a move of 400).

3 The winner is the first player to reach or pass 1000.

4 A similar game can be played with three ten-sided dice to generate a three-digit start number.

5 Any version of the game can be played as 'count back': the starting point is either 100 or 1000 and the winner is the first player to reach zero (or would pass zero with their move; for example a player on 43 rolling a 100 would win).

Count on

Cut out the four number line sections and glue them together where shown to make a 0–100 tabletop number line. Each player will need a number line.

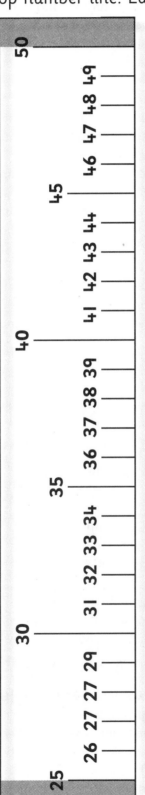
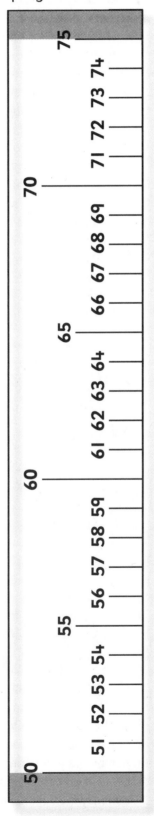

Grouping
Small group working in pairs with adult

Resources
One set of number sequence cards (photocopiable page 25 enlarged to A3) (No two the same within the group)

Vocabulary
sequence
continue
predict
pattern
rule

6. What next?

Teaching input

An essential part of this game is the discussion between the children themselves and the children and adult. In preparation for the game show the children a simple sequence of numbers, for example: 1, 3, 5, 7, 9.

Talk with them about the 'rule' for the sequence, that is, what they can say about it in general terms:
- 'It goes up in twos'
- 'Some numbers are missing'
- 'There's a number missing between two of them' and so on

Only reject a statement if it is actually wrong, but help children to refine their statements to be more accurate.

Ask them to predict the next number and say how they know: 'The next number is 11 because it's two more (than 9)' would be correct.

Ask questions such as 'If there were 8 numbers in the sequence what would the last one be?' and talk about how they know this.

Finally, ask the same kind of questions about a sequence that has been mixed up, for example: 8, 14, 2, 11, 5.

Help them to recognise that is it more difficult to spot the 'rule' when the numbers are not in order and that ordering them will make it easier.

Note: The scoring system can be dispensed with if preferred.

NNS FRAMEWORK OBJECTIVES

Game objective
- Solve simple mathematical problems or puzzles, recognise and predict from simple patterns and relationships.

Year 3 objective
- Solve mathematical problems or puzzles, recognise simple patterns and relationships, generalise and predict.

Links to Unit Plan
Year 3 Spring term
Unit 8 Counting, properties of numbers and reasoning about numbers.

HOW TO PLAY

1 Each pair shuffles their cards and places them face down in a line on the table.
2 Each pair turns over one card and makes a guess as to what the number sequence might be and what numbers it starts and finishes with.
3 Each pair turns over a second card and revises their guess if necessary.
4 This process is continued until all the cards have been turned over.
5 The adult awards points (optional and flexible) according to when the sequence, including start and end numbers, was correctly guessed (four points after two cards, three points after three cards, two points after four cards, and one point if all five had to be revealed).
6 Additional points are awarded if the pairs can correctly predict the next two numbers in the sequence and/or generalise the rule.

Progression towards the Year 3 objective

- Use longer/more complex sequences according to the needs of the children.
- Use sequences with both similarities and differences (for example, sequence of even numbers/sequence of odd numbers – both go up in twos but starting numbers are different).
- Use simple sequences but with a number missing, an extra point is gained by correctly identifying the missing number.

What next?

Sequence 1

| 3 | 6 | 9 | 12 | 15 |

Sequence 2

| 4 | 6 | 8 | 10 | 12 |

Sequence 3

| 10 | 20 | 30 | 40 | 50 |

Sequence 4

| 1 | 4 | 7 | 10 | 13 |

Sequence 5

| 10 | 15 | 20 | 25 | 30 |

Sequence 6

| 7 | 9 | 11 | 13 | 15 |

7. Your money or mine?

Grouping
Pairs

Resources
● One dice
● A selection of 1p, 2p, 5p and 10p coins
● Game board (photocopiable page 27)

Vocabulary
coin
penny
pence
amount
pay
change
odd
even

Teaching input

Remind the children of what is meant by odd and even numbers, and practise recognition of odd and even numbers up to 10. Also practise making up small amounts of money using 1p, 2p, 5p and 10p coins. This can be done with the whole class using large card coins. The children who are going to play the game need to practise giving change from small amounts, for example, change from 10p when paying 6p.

HOW TO PLAY

1 Each player begins with 20p in their piggy bank, made up of 1 x 10p, 1 x 5p, 1 x 2p and 3 x 1p coins.

2 One player chooses to be **odd** and the other **even.**

3 In turn, players roll the dice. If it shows an even number the player who has chosen to be even takes that amount of money from the other player. Similarly the 'odd' player takes the money from the 'even' player if the dice throw is odd.

4 When one player runs out of money, the other player wins.

5 Taking money from the other player may involve giving change.

NNS FRAMEWORK OBJECTIVES

Game objectives
● Use mental strategies to solve simple problems set in 'real life' money or measurement contexts.
● Recognise coins of different values.
● Find totals and change from up to 20p.
● Work out how to pay an exact sum using smaller coins.

Year 3 objective
● Solve word problems involving money, including finding totals, giving change, and working out which coins to pay.

Links to Unit Plan
Year 3 Spring term
Unit 9 Multiplication and division

Progression towards the Year 3 objective

● Each player starts with 50p made up of 1 x 20p, 1 x 10p, 2 x 5p, 3 x 2p and 4 x 1p coins. Two dice are used and the numbers added to give the amount of money to be transferred.

● The start amount can be increased to meet the needs and abilities of the children. As this amount increases, it will be necessary to use different dice. Two ten-sided dice will generate amounts of money up to 99p.

Your money or mine?

Player 1 (Odd)

Player 2 (Even)

8. Does it go?

Grouping
Pairs

Resources
● One dice marked 2, 2, 2, 10, 10, 10
● Counters in two different colours
● A game board (photocopiable page 29)
● Interactive Teaching Program 'Number Grid' (optional)

Vocabulary
even
multiple of

Teaching input

Using a number line and a hundred square, help the children to use counting skills and patterns first to count on in steps of 2, 5 and 10, and then begin to recognise the multiples of these numbers. Where necessary, provide the children with a number line or hundred square to help them in the game.

HOW TO PLAY

1 In turn, players roll the dice and cover a multiple of that number on the grid with a counter in their colour.

2 The first player to have three counters in a straight line of connecting squares (vertically, horizontally or diagonally) is the winner.

NNS FRAMEWORK OBJECTIVES

Game objective
● Begin to recognise odd and even numbers to about 20 as every other number.

Year 3 objective
● Recognise two-digit and three-digit multiples of 2, 5 or 10 and three digit multiples of 50 and 100.

Links to Unit Plan
Year 3 Summer term Unit 8 Counting, properties of numbers and number sequences. Reasoning about numbers

Progression towards the Year 3 objective

● Make a larger grid containing more numbers and including multiples of 5 as well as 2 and 10. Use a dice marked 2, 2, 5, 5, 10, 10.

● Vary the game to include multiples of 50 and 100 and use dice marked accordingly (2, 5, 10, 50, 100 and blank, the blank being used as any of these numbers, when the child has to elect a number and show it divides exactly into their chosen grid number, or miss a turn).

Does it go?

2	50	20	14	30
40	12	4	50	22
18	60	40	6	70
80	8	90	4	16
20	30	2	26	10
12	24	10	30	28

9. What's it got?

Grouping
Pairs

Resources
● Set of number cards 1–20
● Scoring sheet
(photocopiable page 31)

Vocabulary
odd
even
multiple
less than
more than

Teaching input

Using a set of number cards, or the numbers on a classroom number line, invite children in turns to select a number of their choice. Ask them to say first whether it is odd or even and, if the number is greater than 10, how they know (they may, for example, know that numbers ending in 2, 4, 6, 8 or 0 are even, or they may arrive at their decision by counting).

Point out other things about the chosen number, appropriate to the children's knowledge and understanding:
● 'It is in the 3 times table'
● 'It is smaller than 15'
● 'It comes between 7 and 9' and so on.
Some children may be able to make statements of their own about the chosen number.

HOW TO PLAY

1 Shuffle the number cards and place them face down in a pile.
2 In turn, players take the top card and complete the scoring sheet by entering the number and ticking the relevant columns.
3 One point is scored for each tick and the total for that number entered in the final column.
4 When all the cards have been used, the player with the greater total is the winner.

NNS FRAMEWORK OBJECTIVES

Game objective
● Begin to recognise odd and even numbers to about 20 as every other number.

Year 3 objective
● Recognise two-digit and three-digit multiples of 2, 5 or 10 and three digit multiples of 50 and 100.

Links to Unit Plan
Year 3 Summer term
Unit 8 Counting, properties of numbers and number sequences. Reasoning about numbers

Progression towards the Year 3 objective
● Make score sheets with additional or alternative columns such as 'multiple of two/five/ten, less than/greater than other numbers (such as 50).
● Use a pair of ten-sided dice to generate bigger numbers.
● Make a set of cards containing a selection of 3 digit numbers, some of which are multiples of 50 and 100 and adjust the column headings accordingly.

What's it got?

Player 1

Number	Is it odd?	Does it end in 0?	Is it less than 10?	Total score
7	✓	✗	✓	2
			Total score	

Player 2

Number	Is it odd?	Does it end in 0?	Is it less than 10?	Total score
13	✓	✗	✗	1
			Total score	

10. Shape match

Grouping
Groups of 2, 3 or 4 children

Resources
● Two sets of shapes cards (photocopiable page 33)
● Interactive Teaching Program 'Polygon' (optional)

Vocabulary
side
corner
right angle
line of symmetry

Teaching input
Spend a little time with the children looking at the shapes to be used in the game and discussing their properties. Ask questions such as:
● 'Which of these shapes has 4 sides?'
● 'Can you find a shape with 3 corners?'
● 'Are there any shapes that have a right angle?'
● 'Which shapes have a line of symmetry?'
   Children should be encouraged to use the names of shapes where appropriate.

HOW TO PLAY
These cards can be used to play Snap or Matching Pairs (Pelmanism)
At the start of the game choose the feature or property that will give a snap or a match, for example,
● Shapes with 3, 4, 5 or 6 sides
● Shapes with 3, 4, 5, or 6 corners
● Shapes with at least one right angle
● Shapes with 1 line of symmetry or those with no lines of symmetry.

NNS FRAMEWORK OBJECTIVES

Game objective
● Sort shapes and describe some of their features, such as the number of sides and corners, symmetry and other properties.

Year 4 unit objective
● Classify polygons using criteria such as number of right angles, whether or not they are regular, symmetry properties.

Links to Unit Plan
Year 4 Autumn term
Unit 4 Reasoning about shape

Progression towards the Year 4 objective
● Increase the level of difficulty of the features needed for a match (for example, exactly one pair of parallel lines, at least two acute angles, regular shapes).
● Focus on two features simultaneously (for example, two pairs of parallel lines but no right angles, four sides and exactly one right angle).

Shape match

11. Odds and evens

Grouping
Pairs

Resources
● A set of double six dominoes with the double blank removed
● A recording sheet (photocopiable page 35)

Vocabulary
odd
even
total

Teaching input

Prior to playing the game, practise with the children counting forwards and backwards in twos from and back to zero and from and back to one.

Discuss which of these numbers are even and which are odd.

Use counters to show that even numbers can be arranged in pairs but odd numbers cannot (there will always be an 'odd one out').

Practise again, saying all the even numbers to ten and all the odd numbers to ten, to help the children remember them.

When children have completed a game, look with them at the numbers recorded as the totals for each domino. Lead them to the 'discovery' that all the numbers are even, including the 'odd' dominoes.

This discussion could be extended to include what would happen if one of the numbers on the domino was even and the other was odd. The recording sheet could be used to support the children's investigations.

HOW TO PLAY

1 Players decide who will be 'odd' and who will be 'even'.
2 Turn all the dominoes face down and shuffle them.
3 In turn, players select a domino, turn it face up and consider the numbers on each half of the domino.
4 The 'odd' player may keep it if both halves of the domino show an odd number (for example the 5,3 domino) and the 'even' player may keep it if both halves of the domino show an even number. The domino is recorded on the score sheet.
5 Otherwise, the domino is returned to the middle face down and the other player takes a turn.
6 The game ends when a player's score sheet is full and s/he is then the winner.

NNS FRAMEWORK OBJECTIVES

Game objective
● Count on in twos, from and back to zero or any small number. Recognise odd and even numbers to at least 30.

Year 4 unit objective
● Recognise odd and even numbers up to 1000 and some of their properties, including the outcome of sums or differences of pairs of odd/even numbers.

Links to Unit Plan
Year 4 Autumn term Unit 8 Properties of numbers and number sequences. Reasoning about numbers

Progression towards the Year 4 objective

● Players collect dominoes as before but may keep it only if the total number of spots is odd or even.
● Play the games with two standard dice showing numerals instead of spots. Players collect counters instead of keeping dominoes.
● When children are ready to progress to larger numbers, each player in turn rolls two ten-sided dice twice to generate two two-digit numbers. (For example, 9 and 6 would represent either 69 or 96. 4 and 3 would represent 43 or 34.) The player enters the numbers as O (odd) or E (even) on the score sheet, predicts whether the total will be odd or even, and enters O or E as the total. The other player checks the total with a calculator and a counter is collected if the prediction was correct.

Odds and evens

Player A

3	1	total	4
		total	
		total	
		total	
		total	
		total	
		total	
		total	
		total	
		total	

Player B

2	4	total	6
		total	
		total	
		total	
		total	
		total	
		total	
		total	
		total	
		total	

12. Doubles and halves

Grouping
Groups of up to 6 children

Resources
● Bingo cards:
● The cards for games 1–4 are on pages 37–40. There are five cards on each sheet, one for each child and each containing six or eight numbers.
● Counters
● Dice appropriate to the game (see specific instructions on game boards)

Vocabulary
double
half
halve

Teaching input

Practise doubling and halving with the children. Doubles and halves of smaller numbers should gradually be memorised. When working with larger numbers, doubling and halving strategies should be revised and practised. Those children who need a support resource should have a number line and/or counters to hand to help with doubling and halving small numbers they have not yet memorised.

HOW TO PLAY

These games are all played as a standard game of bingo with one child acting as caller and the others (up to 5), crossing off or covering numbers on their cards. Numbers are generated by rolling the dice appropriate to the game and then doubled or halved according to the instructions. Information about deciding the winner is given on each sheet. It is very important to ensure that each child understands how they can win. In the halving games, as an alternative to missing a turn if an odd number is called, the caller can be instructed to add one to any odd number (for example, if a 3 is rolled, the caller says 4).

Progression towards the Year 4 objective

When children are ready to go on to bigger numbers, the game can be varied as follows:
● Each pair of children has a copy of the 100 square game board on page 41
● In turn, players generate a two digit number by rolling two ten-sided dice (a roll of 6 and 5 could represent 65 or 56) and decide whether to double or halve the number. They then cross off their doubled or halved number, or cover it, on the 100 square game board
● If a player cannot cross off or cover a number because all possibilities have already been crossed off or covered, s/he misses a turn.
● The winner is the first to cross off or cover four numbers in a row (horizontally, vertically or diagonally).

Note: In this version, some numbers can only be doubled, and some can only be halved. The only combinations which cannot be used at all are 5/5, 5/7, 5/9, 7/7, 7/9 and 9/9. If a player rolls these combinations s/he misses a turn. All other combinations can be used – for example, a roll of 7/3 can be used as 37 and doubled.

NNS FRAMEWORK OBJECTIVES

Game objective
● Know by heart the doubles of all numbers to ten and the corresponding halves. Derive quickly doubles of all numbers to at least 15.

Year 4 unit objective
● Use doubling or halving, starting from known facts.

Links to Unit Plan
Year 4 Autumn term
Unit 9 Multiplication and division

Doubles and halves (1)

Game 1: Doubles to 10. Ten-sided dice. Full house to win.

Card 1

18	2	6	20
8	4	16	10

Card 2

2	6	10	14
20	8	12	4

Card 3

8	2	6	16
14	4	20	12

Card 4

6	8	14	18
16	12	4	10

Card 5

2	12	14	18
8	20	10	6

Doubles and halves (2)

Game 2: Halves to 20. Twenty-sided dice. Full house to win.

Card 1

9	1	3	10
4	2	8	5

Card 2

1	3	5	7
10	4	6	2

Card 3

4	1	3	8
7	2	10	6

Card 4

3	4	7	9
8	6	2	5

Card 5

1	6	7	9
4	10	5	3

Doubles and halves (3)

Game 3: Doubles to 6. Six-sided dice. Horizontal line wins.

Card 1

2	10	8
6	4	12

Card 2

4	12	10
8	6	2

Card 3

12	8	6
4	2	10

Card 4

6	4	2
12	8	10

Card 5

8	5	4
2	2	6

Doubles and halves (4)

Game 4: Halves to 12. Twelve-sided dice. Horizontal line wins.

Card 1

1	5	14
3	2	6

Card 2

2	6	5
4	3	1

Card 3

6	4	3
2	1	5

Card 4

3	2	1
6	4	5

Card 5

4	2	6
1	5	3

Doubles and halves (5)

1	2	3	4	5	6	7	8	9	10
11	12	13	14	15	16	17	18	19	20
21	22	23	24	25	26	27	28	29	30
31	33	33	34	35	36	37	38	39	40
41	42	43	44	45	46	47	48	49	50
51	52	53	54	55	56	57	58	59	60
61	62	63	64	65	66	67	68	69	70
71	72	73	74	75	76	77	78	79	80
81	82	83	84	85	86	87	88	89	90
91	92	93	94	95	96	97	98	99	100

13. Mass matters

Grouping
Pairs

Resources
Each pair of children will need:
● Weighing scales with a simple graduated dial
● A selection of objects of different weights under 1kg
● A recording sheet (photocopiable page 43)
● Calculator (optional)
● Interactive Teaching Program 'Measuring Scales' (optional)

Vocabulary
mass
weight
kilogram
gram
scales
estimate

Teaching input
Discuss what is meant by an estimate (a sensible guess) and that an estimate cannot be 'right' or 'wrong' – estimates are either good or poor. Discuss also the difference between an estimate and an accurate measurement (which *can* be right or wrong). If appropriate to the children's ability, practical situations requiring an estimate and those requiring accurate measurement could also be discussed. Children should be aware that in the majority of situations they will meet in their day to day lives, an estimate is more appropriate (and useful) than an accurate measurement. Point out to the children that the use and understanding of estimates and measurement applies to *all* measurement, not just mass.

Note: A set of weights clearly marked as 10g, 20g, 50g, 100g, 500g and 1kg could be provided to help with estimation.

HOW TO PLAY
1 Player A estimates the weight of an object in grams and records it on the sheet.
2 Player B weighs the same object (to the nearest labelled division on the dial) and writes its weight on the sheet.
3 Together they work out the difference between the estimate and the actual weight (using a calculator if necessary) and this number is player A's score.
4 Player B then estimates the weight of another object and player A checks it by weighing.
5 Play continues in this way until all the objects have been weighed. The scores are totalled (again using a calculator if needed) and the winner is the player with the **lowest** score.

NNS FRAMEWORK OBJECTIVES

Game objective
● Estimate, measure and compare masses using standard units. Read a simple scale to the nearest labelled division.

Year 4 unit objective
● Record estimates and readings from scales to a suitable degree of accuracy.

Links to Unit Plan
Year 4 Spring term
Unit 4 Measures – time, mass and area

Progression towards the Year 4 objective
This game can be played at any level and to increasing degrees of accuracy. Some examples might be:
● The player weighing the objects must give a reading to the nearest 10g, for example, or to the nearest 5g. (Much will depend on how the dial is marked and the accuracy of the weighing scales).
● Use objects weighing more than and less than 1kg.
● Estimates can be given as, for example, more than half a kilogram or less than half a kilogram (a point being gained for a correct estimate).
● Estimates must be given in two ways, for example, as 1kg 350g or 1350g, scoring as for the basic game but with a bonus point for correctly writing the estimate in two ways.

Mass matters

Player A			Player B		
Estimate	Actual	Score	Estimate	Actual	Score
500g	350g	150	400g	380g	20

14. Five to win

Grouping
Groups of 4 to 6 children

Resources
● Each child will need one of the strips of 5 pictures (photocopiable page 45)
● Each group needs one dice and some counters
● Interactive Teaching Program 'Counting On and Back' (optional)

Vocabulary
count on
count back

Teaching input
Before the game begins, it is useful to have some basic practice in counting from and back to numbers other than zero or one.

HOW TO PLAY

1 The first player rolls the dice and says the number (for example 4).
2 The player to his or her left says '5', the next person says '6' and so on until the count reaches 10.
3 The player who says 10 places a counter on one of their pictures.
4 The player to the left of the first player (not the last player to speak) rolls the dice to start the next count.
5 The winner is the first person to cover all five pictures.

NNS FRAMEWORK OBJECTIVES

Game objective
● Describe and extend simple number sequences; count on or back in ones or tens, starting from any two-digit number.

Year 4 unit objective
● Recognise and extend number sequences formed by counting from any number in steps of constant size, extending beyond zero when counting back.

Links to Unit Plan
Year 4 Spring term
Unit 8 Properties of numbers.
Reasoning about numbers

Progression towards the Year 4 objective
There are many possible variations to this game:
● Use two different coloured dice, one to start the count, the other to give the step size (for example, blue dice gives start number 3, red dice gives step size 5, so the count is 3, 8, 13, 18... and the person who says the first number past 20 gets a counter).
● Use one or two ten-sided dice to give the start number and one or two standard dice to give the step size.
● Use two ten-sided dice to generate a two-digit number and count on in 10s; the first to pass 100 gets the counter.
● Count backwards. Children not yet able to recognise negative numbers will stop the count at the 'last number' they can say (for example, backwards count in threes from 8 would be 8, 5, 2, with the player saying 2 getting the counter).
    Different versions can be devised to meet the needs and abilities of the children.

Five to win

15. Tables test

Teaching input

Practise with the children counting in twos, fives and tens, and, if appropriate, show them how to use a multiplication grid. A grid could also be used during the game for those children only just beginning to memorise their 2, 5 and 10 times-tables. As they grow in confidence and learn more facts, the grid can be withdrawn.

HOW TO PLAY

1 Children learning the two and ten times-tables use grid 1, those also learning the 5 times-table use grid 2.
2 In turn, players roll the dice and multiply the number it shows by 2 or 10 (or 5 if using grid 2) to make one of the numbers in the grid.
3 That number is covered with a counter.
4 If a player throws a zero the turn is missed.
5 The winner is the first player to have three counters in a line, horizontally, vertically or diagonally.

Progression towards the Year 4 objective

Use the 100 square on page 41 instead of the grids. Players must multiply their dice throw by 2, 3, 4, 5 or 10 to match a number in the hundred square. The winner is the first player to have four counters in a line.

Tables test

Grid 1

18	80	20	8	30
40	6	10	14	90
30	2	18	50	18
16	12	70	30	4
2	60	20	10	6

Grid 2

30	5	2	75	60
50	12	90	25	16
4	70	35	85	10
15	6	55	14	65
18	80	20	8	40

16. Ups and downs

Grouping
Pairs

Resources
● One dice
● Two counters of different colour
● Game board (photocopiable page 49)

Vocabulary
round up/down
nearest
round to the nearest 10/100

Teaching input

Discuss with the children how they know whether a number should be rounded up or down. Initially use questions such as, ' Is the number 24 nearer to 20 or 30?' This can be answered easily by counting on a number line how many steps away 24 is from 20 and 30. At first, avoid numbers ending in a 5 and when the children are ready, introduce the idea that 25, for example, is an equal number of steps away from both 20 and 30. Say that in this case we have to have a rule. The rule is that numbers 'in the middle' (those ending in 5) round up to the next multiple of 10, not down to the previous one.

The game board can be modified to help children who are still learning to deal with rounding, especially with numbers ending in 5. You could highlight the multiples of 10, or colour numbers which should be rounded *down* in one colour and those which should be rounded *up* in another colour.

HOW TO PLAY

1 In turn, players roll the dice and move that number of spaces forward along the board.
2 If the number landed on is less than 5 or ends in a number less than 5 the player must go back to the last multiple of 10 (for example on 3, go back to 0, on 24, go back to 20).
3 If the number landed on is 5 or more, or ends in the number 5 or more the player moves on to the next multiple of 10 (for example on 6 move on to 10, on 75 move on to 80).
4 The winner is the first player to reach 100.

Progression towards the Year 4 objective

● Change the instructions so as not to involve the number 5. Each player in turn rolls the dice and moves that number of spaces forward along the board.
● The number landed on is rounded to the nearest 10 and the player moves their counter to the appropriate multiple of 10.
● To involve three digit numbers rounded to the nearest 100, the game needs to be adapted as follows:
1   Players roll three ten-sided dice to generate a three-digit number.
Note: Any roll of three digits not including zero can be used in any combination but a roll involving zero cannot be used to make a two-digit number; for example 0, 4 and 8 can only be used as 408, 804, 480 or 840.
2   The score for any turn is the nearest multiple of 100. The player may choose which 3 digit number from the possible combinations is to be rounded to produce the score (for example, a roll of 2, 5 and 7 could be used as 752 to score 800 or as 527 to score 500, and so on).
3   The winner is the player who, by adding or subtracting each score to their previous total, reaches exactly 1000.

NNS FRAMEWORK OBJECTIVES

Game objective
● Round numbers less than 100 to the nearest 10.

Year 4 unit objective
● Round any positive integer less than 1000 to the nearest 10 or 100.

Links to Unit Plan
Year 4 Summer term
Unit 1 Place value

Ups and downs

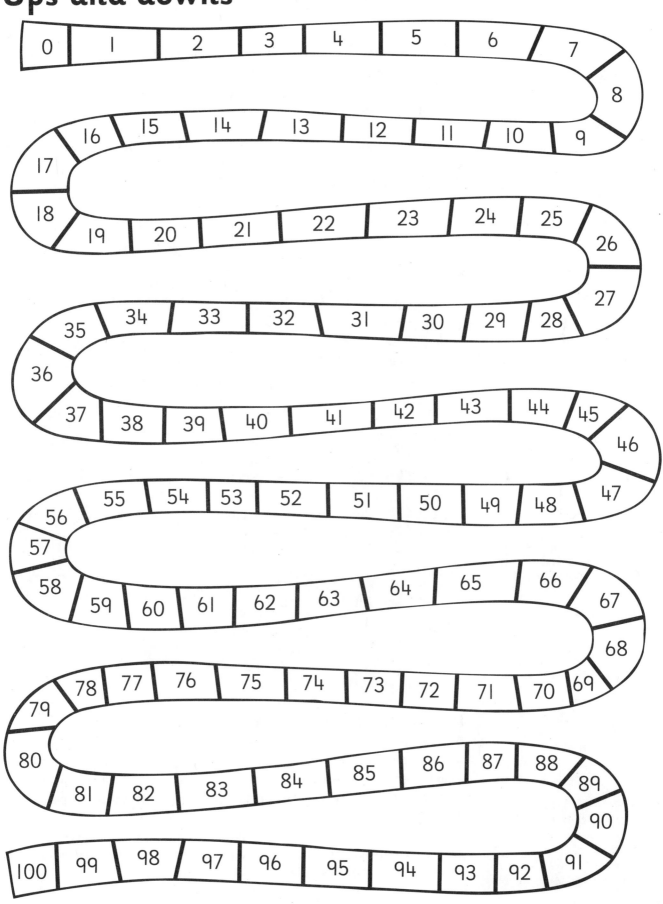

17. Take two

Grouping
Pairs

Resources
● Pencil and paper
● Calculator for checking
● Game board (photocopiable page 51). Children can colour the 'zones' before the game is played, or they can be separated and copied on to red and green paper.
● Interactive Teaching Programs 'Number Line' and 'Number Grid' (optional).

Vocabulary
multiple of 10
near multiple of 10
adjust

Teaching input
Revise with the children how to add or subtract 9, 10 and 11 and how this helps them to add and subtract 19 and 21. For example:

$28 + 9 = 28 + 10 - 1$
$57 - 21 = 57 - 20 - 1$
$86 - 9 = 86 - 10 + 1$

A number line and a 100 square are useful support resources when practising addition and subtraction strategies. Some children may need to use one or other of these resources as they are playing the game.

HOW TO PLAY

1 In turn, players choose one number from the red zone and one from the green zone and add them together. The aim is to have a total as near as possible to 50 but smaller than 50. The totals can be checked by the other player using a calculator.
2 The player who has the total nearer to 50 scores one point.
3 Play continues in this way to an agreed end point (say after 5 turns each). Neither player may use the same combination of two numbers they have used before (they may, however, use either one of them paired with a different number). 4 Choices can be indicated by placing counters of that player's chosen colour on the appropriate numbers.
5 The same children should also play a difference version of the game, the aim being, for example, for one player to have a larger/smaller difference between the two numbers than the other in order to win a point.

NNS FRAMEWORK OBJECTIVES

Game objectives
● Add/subtract 9 or 11: add/subtract 10 and adjust by 1.
● Begin to add/subtract 19 or 21: add/subtract 20 and adjust by 1.

Year 4 unit objective
● Use known number facts and place value, to add or subtract mentally, including any pair of two digit whole numbers.

Links to Unit Plan
Year 4 Summer term Unit 2 Addition and subtraction

Progression towards the Year 4 objective
● Change the rule so that the aim is to have a total greater than 50.
● Make a game board showing **any** two digit numbers in the green zone and including additional near multiples of 10 in the red zone (ensuring that no two when added together will total more than 100). The winner will be the player with the total nearer to 100.
● Make a game board showing a selection of any two digit numbers in each zone so that players practise other addition and subtraction strategies. The winner could be the player with the higher/lower total.

Take two

Red zone

9	11	20
21	10	19

Green zone

27	34	26
36	25	37

18. Snakes and arrows

Grouping
Pairs

Resources
● Pencil and paper
● One dice marked with the numbers 2, 5, 8, 12, 15 and 19
● One ruler
● Counters
● Game board 1 (photocopiable page 53) enlarged to A3 so that the arrows measure as follows: A = 2cm, B = 5cm, C = 8cm, D = 12cm, E = 15cm and F = 19cm

Vocabulary
measure
guess
estimate
about
roughly
approximately
just over/under

Teaching input
Remind the children of what is meant by an estimate and spend a little time estimating the length of items around the classroom.

Remind them also of how to measure straight lines with a ruler, pointing out particularly that the 0 mark is the starting point for the measurement, not the end of the ruler. Allow some time for practice.

HOW TO PLAY

1 Player 1 rolls the dice and estimates which arrow measures that number of centimetres.

2 Player 2 measures to check.

3 Player 1 takes two counters if s/he has identified the correct arrow and one counter if the arrow chosen measures 3cm more or less. A difference of 4cm does not score. (For example: Player 1 rolls a 12 and chooses arrow E. Player 2 measures this arrow and finds it is actually 15cm. Player 1 collects one counter.)

4 Players reverse roles and repeat.

5 Play continues in this way until one player has collected, say, ten counters.

NNS FRAMEWORK OBJECTIVES

Game objectives
● Estimate, measure and compare lengths, masses and capacities, using standard units.

Year 4 unit objectives
● Suggest suitable units and measuring equipment to estimate or measure length, mass or capacity.
● Record estimates and readings from scales to a suitable degree of accuracy.

Links to Unit Plan
Year 4 Summer term
Unit 4 Measures

Progression towards the Year 4 objective
● Make a game board with 20 arrows ranging in length from 1cm to 20cm inclusive and use a 20-sided dice. If players identify the right arrow to match the dice roll, they score 2. If they identify an arrow within 1cm of the actual measurement they score 1. Any greater difference does not score at all.
● Make a game board with arrows measuring both whole and half centimetres.
● Use 'Snakes and arrows' 2 and 3 on photocopiable pages 54 and 55 (enlarged). Initially discuss with the children how they are going to measure the snakes and then provide the equipment they choose to use (for example, string).

Snakes and arrows (1)

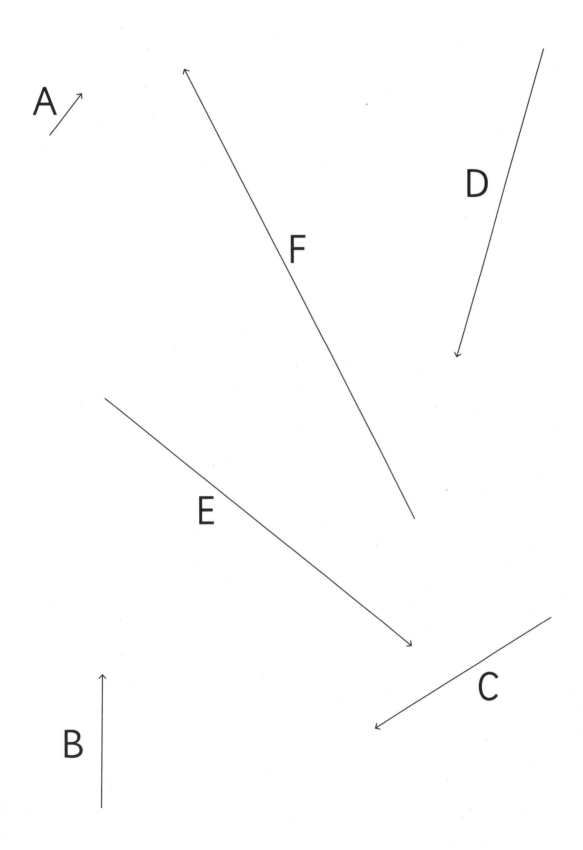

Snakes and arrows (2)

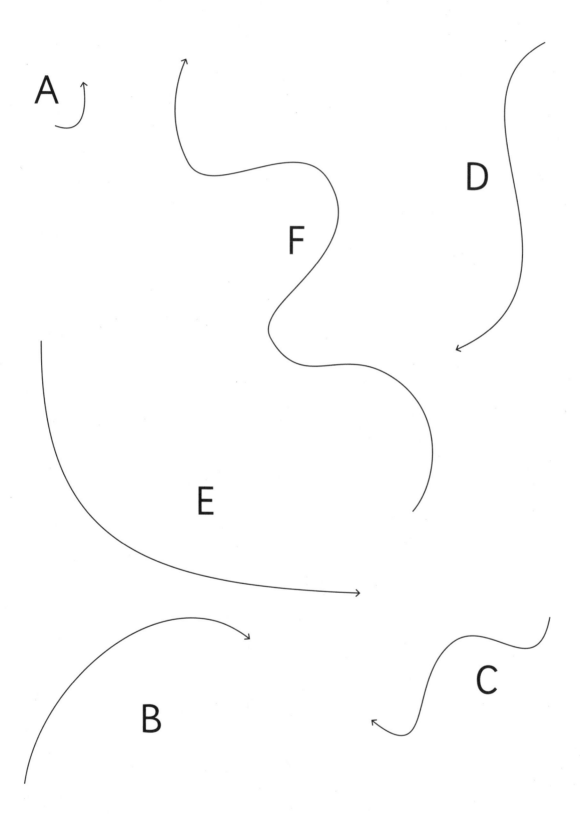

Snakes and arrows (3)

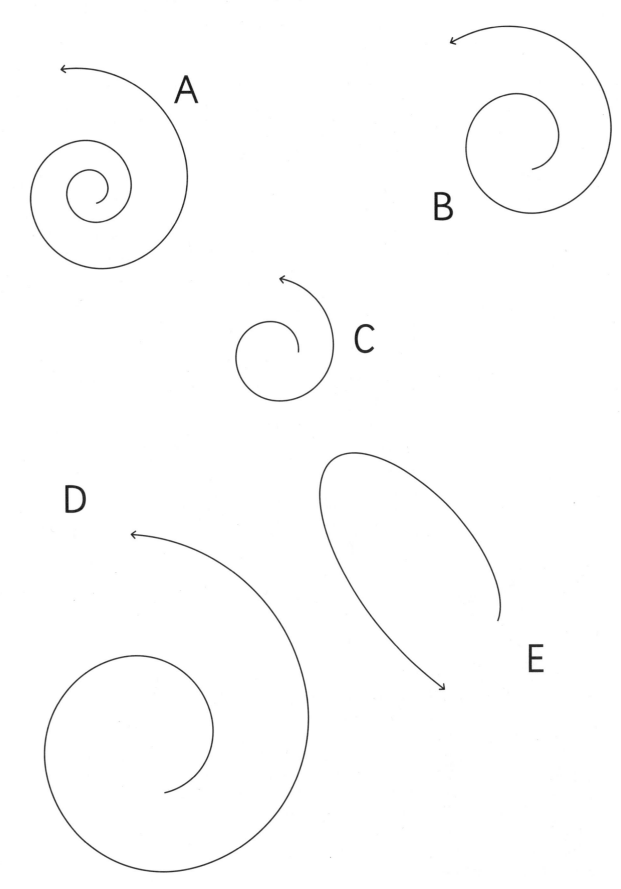

19. Shoot the digits

Grouping
Pairs

Resources
Each pair of children will need:
● Calculator
● Pencil and paper
● Counters
● Arrow cards (optional)
● Recording sheet
(photocopiable page 57)

● Interactive Teaching
Program 'Place Value'
(optional)

Vocabulary
units
ones
tens
hundreds
digit
value
calculator display

Teaching input
Remind the children of what each digit in a three digit number is worth. Demonstrate with a calculator how to 'shoot' the digits to zero by subtracting their value (for example, to 'shoot' the 5 in 356 a player must subtract 50 leaving 306 in the display). Point out that when 'shooting' the hundreds digit it will not be replaced with a zero. Demonstrate with arrow cards why this happens. Show children how to use arrow cards to help them during the game (optional).

HOW TO PLAY

1 Player A enters a three digit number in the calculator display (no zeros), records the number on the recording sheet and passes the calculator to player B.
2 Player B must 'shoot' one of the digits by subtracting its value. S/he records the move made and passes the calculator back to player A.
3 Player A 'shoots' one of the remaining digits, records the move and passes the calculator back to player B who 'shoots' the final digit leaving 0 in the display.
4 Player B enters another three digit number and round two begins.
5 The game ends when the recording sheet is full.

Scoring:
For each successful 'shot' the player collects a counter. If a player makes a mistake s/he loses one counter and the round is restarted with the same start number.

NNS FRAMEWORK OBJECTIVES

Game objective
● Read and write whole numbers to at least 1000 in figures and words, and know what each digit represents.

Year 5 unit objective
● Read and write whole numbers in figures and words, and know what each digit represents.

Links to Unit Plan
Year 5 Autumn term
Unit 1 Place value

Progression towards the Year 5 objective
● Increase the size of the start number to four digits and then beyond until the children are using numbers appropriate to their understanding.
● Vary the game so that the aim is to reverse the digits by adding and subtracting, rather than to reduce the number to zero. For example, with a start number of 3582 and target number of 2853, appropriate steps would be:
1 Subtract 30 to give 3552.
2 Subtract 1000 to give 2552.
3 Add 300 to give 2852.
4 Add 1 to give 2853.

Shoot the digits

	Start number	Step one	Step two	Step three
	356	-50	-6	-300
1				
2				
3				
4				
5				
6				
7				
8				
9				
10				

20. Hexed

Teaching input

Revise and practise rounding two-digit numbers to the nearest 10, remembering that numbers ending in 5 round up, not down.

Explain to the children how this will help them to play the game.

Choose a two-digit and a one-digit number from outside the grid, for example, 31 and 5. Estimate the answer to 31 x 5 by rounding 31 to 30. 30 multiplied by 5 is 150 so the answer to 31 x 5 will be a little more than this.

Ask the children to try a few more examples (with help if necessary).

Point out that if players choose numbers at random they are unlikely to win. They should look at the numbers in the hexagons and use rounding and estimating skills to help them choose wisely.

Remind them that when working out estimates they should use known calculation strategies, for example, to multiply by 4 they can double and double again.

Grouping
Pairs or groups of 4

Resources
Each pair or group of 4 children will need:
● Game board (photocopiable page 59)
● Counters in two colours
● A calculator (optional)

Vocabulary
product
multiply
round to the nearest
estimate
approximate

HOW TO PLAY

1 The object of the game is to create a connecting line of counters across the grid from one side to the other, starting from the 'start' hexagon.

2 In order to place a counter, players must choose two of the numbers outside the hexagon grid whose product is the same as a number in a hexagon.

3 In turn, each player chooses one single digit number and one two-digit number from outside the grid and estimates their product by rounding.

4 S/he then checks the calculation (with a calculator if appropriate) and if the product of the two numbers matches a number in one of the hexagons, s/he places a counter on that hexagon.

5 If there is no match, the turn is lost.

6 The winner is the first player to have a connecting line of counters across the grid.

NNS FRAMEWORK OBJECTIVES

Game objective
● Round any two-digit number to the nearest 10 and any three-digit number to the nearest 100.

Year 5 unit objective
● Estimate by approximating (round to the nearest 10 or 100), then check result.

Links to Unit Plan
Year 5 Autumn term Unit 3 Multiplication and division.

Progression towards the Year 5 objective

● Use version 2 (photocopiable page 60) where the players must round the two-digit numbers and perhaps also the single digit numbers (for example, 8 and 9 would round to 10).

● Create new game boards from the blank one provided on photocopiable page 61, by increasing the size of the numbers, (or the number of numbers), first involving more difficult two-digit by one-digit multiplications, and then moving to three-digit by one-digit.

Hexed (version 1)

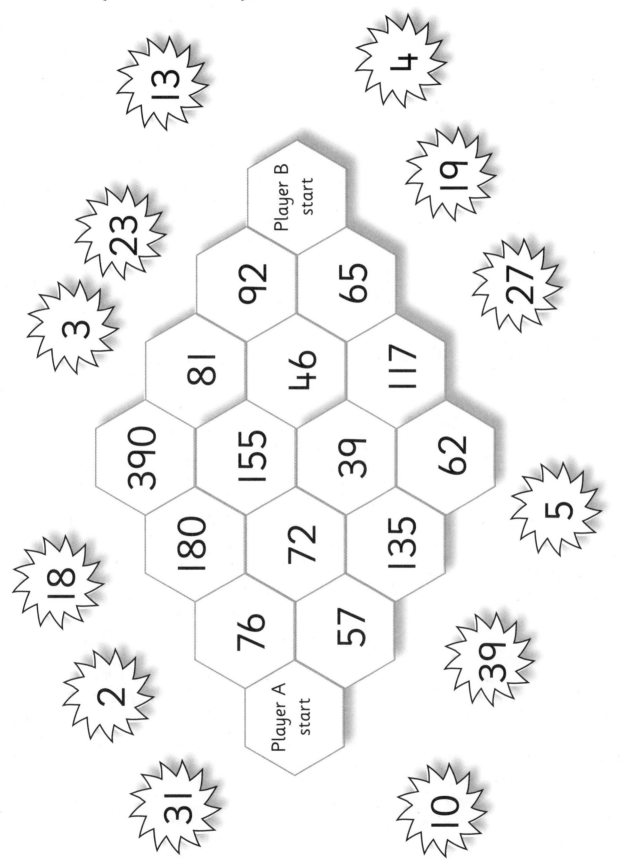

Hexed (version 2)

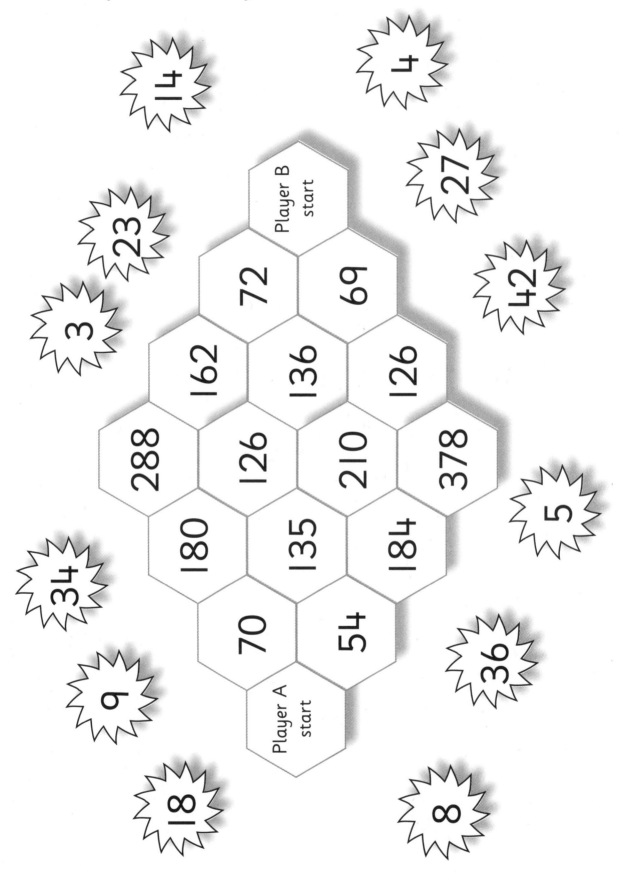

Hexed (blank)

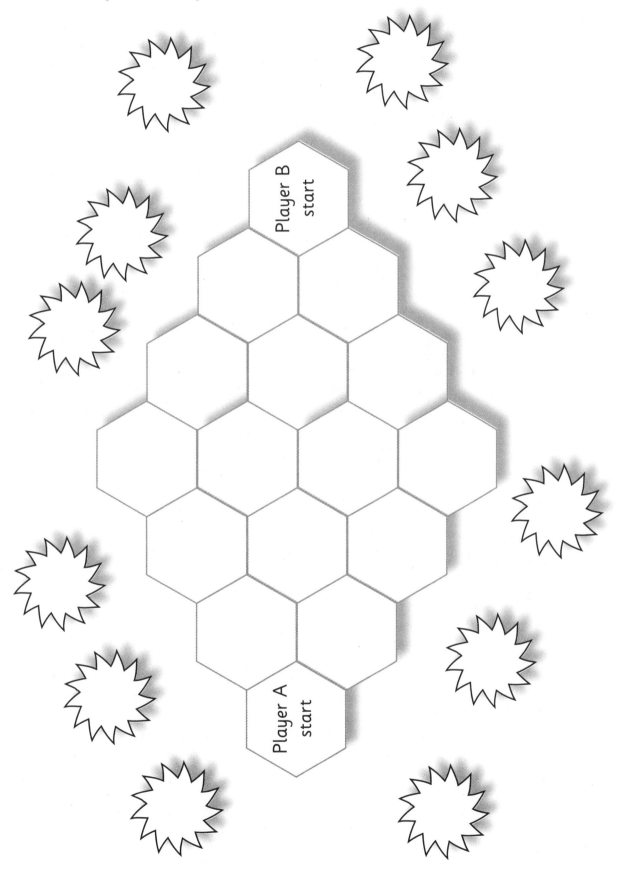

21. All the fours

Grouping
Pairs

Resources
● Game board (photocopiable page 63)
● One dice
● Two counters to move along the board
● A collection of counters for scoring
● Interactive Teaching Program 'Polygon' (optional)

Vocabulary
regular
irregular
quadrilateral
side
straight

Teaching input

Remind the children of the properties of quadrilaterals. Ask questions such as:
● 'How many sides does a quadrilateral have?'
● 'How many corners or vertices does it have?'
● 'Can you remember any names of special quadrilaterals?' (For example, square, rectangle, oblong and so on.)
● 'What can you say about a square?' For example, all sides are equal, all angles are right angles.)

Remind the children that a shape with all its sides and angles equal is called a regular shape. 'Are there any more regular quadrilaterals?' (No.)

HOW TO PLAY

1 Players take turns to roll a dice and move their counter along the track
2 If a player lands on a quadrilateral s/he collects a counter from the 'bank' (optional rule – if that quadrilateral is a square the player collects two counters).
3 The first player to reach the end of the track collects a bonus counter
4 When both players have reached the end of the track, the winner is the one who has collected most counters.

Progression towards the Year 5 objective

Change the scoring system to include some or all of the following:
● Collect one counter for landing on any triangle plus an extra counter if it is isosceles, two extra if it is equilateral.
● Collect two counters for landing on any quadrilateral plus an extra counter if it has 4 right angles.
● Collect three counters for landing on a hexagon plus an extra counter if it is regular.
● Collect five counters for landing on a regular pentagon.
● Change the scoring system in other ways to focus attention on specific properties of 2-D shapes (for example score for symmetrical shapes).
● Produce a game board for quadrilaterals only, awarding points for landing on, say, a quadrilateral with exactly one pair of parallel sides).
● It may be useful to produce 'scoring cards' for the children to refer to, for example a folded, stand-up card illustrating the number of counters for each property (see illustration below).

NNS FRAMEWORK OBJECTIVES

Game objective
● Classify and describe 3-D and 2-D shapes, including quadrilaterals.

Year 5 unit objectives
● Recognise properties of rectangles.
● Classify triangles (isosceles, equilateral, scalene) using criteria such as equal sides and equal angles, lines of symmetry.

Links to Unit Plan
Year 5 Autumn term
Unit 8 Shape and space

3 counters for a hexagon.
1 extra counter if it is regular.

All the fours

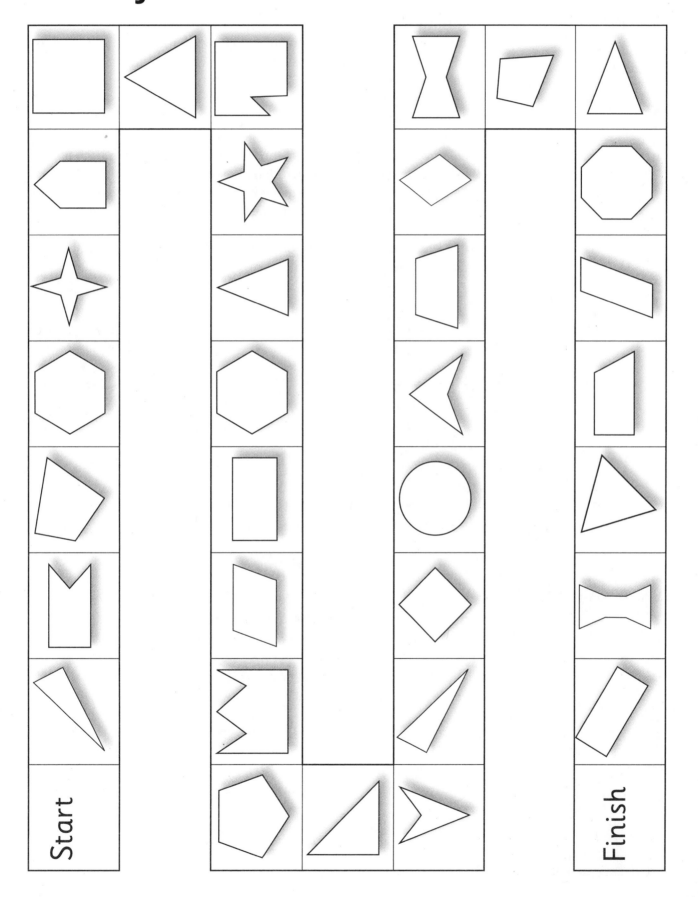

22. More or less?

Grouping
Pairs

Resources
Each pair of children will need:
● Two ten-sided dice
● Recording sheet
(photocopiable page 65)
● Counters
● 1–100 number line
(optional)

● Interactive Teaching
Program 'Ordering Numbers'
(optional)

Vocabulary
more than
less than
equal to
the same as

Teaching input
Practise generating two-digit numbers with two ten-sided dice (for example, when one dice shows 2 and the other 6, the number could be 26 or 62).

Help the children to decide which of the two possible numbers is the bigger either by:
● using a number line
● looking at the tens digit – the units digit has no significance when deciding which is bigger (unless the tens digit is the same in each number – this is not possible when generating numbers with two ten-sided dice).

Ask what numbers could be made with a roll of zero on one dice and, say, 3 on the other. Do we allow 03? Discuss the fact that this would represent no tens and three units, and could therefore be read as 3.

Ask what they will do if both dice show the same number (they then have no choice about what number to make).

HOW TO PLAY
1 In turn, players roll both dice and decide what number to make.
2 When both players have generated a number, they write them in the first box on the recording sheet so that the statement is true.
3 The player whose number appears in the first half of the box wins that round and takes a counter.
4 When all the boxes are full the winner is the player with the most counters.

NNS FRAMEWORK OBJECTIVES

Game objective
● Read and begin to write the vocabulary of comparing and ordering numbers.

Year 5 unit objective
● Use the vocabulary of comparing and ordering numbers, including symbols such as <, >, ≤, ≥ and =.

Links to Unit Plan
Year 5 Spring term
Unit 1 Place value.

Progression towards the Year 5 objective
● Play the game as above but using three ten-sided dice to make three-digit numbers.
● Change the game board so that players must make an extended statement true (using two-digit or three-digit numbers):
□ > □ > □
● Change the game board so that the statements are more complex, for example:
□ < □ > □
● Change the game board so that it involves the symbols ≤ and ≥, for example:
□ ≥ □ ≥ □

(In these versions of the game, players generate three numbers between them and decide on the order, the player who generated the largest number scoring the point for that round.)

More or less

>
<
>
<
>
<
>
<
>
<

<
>
<
>
<
>
<
>
<
>

>
<
>
<
>
<
>
<
>
<

<
>
<
>
<
>
<
>
<
>

23. Factory

Grouping
Groups of 4

Resources
Each group of 4 will need:
● 4 calculators
● A copy of the number grid (photocopiable page 67)
● Counters in four colours

Vocabulary
repeated addition
multiply
divide

NNS FRAMEWORK OBJECTIVES

Game objective
● Understand multiplication as repeated addition.

Year 5 unit objective
● Use factors (for example 8 x 12 = 8 x 4 x 3).

Links to Unit Plan
Year 5 Spring term
Unit 3 Multiplication and division

Teaching input
Show the children how to use the constant function of a calculator:
● Keying in '0 + + 2' will 'tell' the calculator to repeatedly add two starting at 0. On pressing the equals key the display will show 2, pressing the equals key again will produce 4 in the display and so on. So a key sequence of 0 + + 2 = = = = = will show 2, 4, 6, 8, 10.
● To generate odd numbers, the sequence would be 1 + + 2 = = = = =.
● To generate the multiples of 3 key in 0 + + 3 = = = = =.
   Note: Some calculators respond to a slightly different key sequence, but all variations involve some combination of the number to be added, the start number and the + and = keys.

As the children progress towards the Year 5 objective they will need to make the link between repeated addition and multiplication. Demonstrate that 3 + 3 + 3 + 3 + 3 = 15 and that this can be said as 'five lots of three' and written as 5 x 3, or said as '3 counted 5 times' and written as 3 x 5.

Write out, or show them a copy of, the three times-table. Focus on the answers and point out that each answer is three more than the last one, and/or that the pattern of the answers: 3, 6, 9, 12... is an 'add 3' pattern.

HOW TO PLAY

The object of the game is to get three counters in touching squares. These arrangements (or rotations/reflections of them) are winning positions:
1 In turn players choose a number in the grid which they will try to win.
2 The player can win that number by correctly counting on in steps of equal size to reach it (using the constant function on the calculator) Example: A player nominates the number 36 in the grid and sets up the constant 'add 3' so that the display shows 0, 3, 6, 9, 12, 15, 18, 21, 24, 27, 30, 33, 36.
3 Other players check either by multiplication, division, repeated subtraction or repeating the same procedure.
4 If the player misses the target (for example, by setting up the constant 'add 5' to hit the target number 36) s/he does not win that number.
5 When all the numbers in the grid are covered the winner is the player with the most completed groups of three counters.

Progression towards the Year 5 objective
● Players win the numbers by correctly nominating two of its factors. The other players check using a calculator. For example, to win 36, the player can choose 3 and 12, 4 and 9, 6 and 6 and so on.
● Make a game board showing multiplication facts instead of numbers, for example, 7 x 12, 15 x 11, 5 x 16. Players win a square by correctly factorising one of the numbers (such as 5 x 3 x 11). The other players check using a calculator.

Factory

18	30	24	42	12
36	26	50	34	28
22	35	63	16	48
27	44	21	40	64
14	33	70	66	20
45	15	25	49	32

24. Crazy cubes

Grouping
Pairs

Resources
Each pair of children will need:
● Interlocking cubes
● A dice
● Two counters in different colours
● A game board (photocopiable page 69)

Vocabulary
cube
identical
three dimensional

Teaching input
To prepare for the game:
● Give the children a collection of interlocking cubes and allow time for them to explore all the different shapes they can make by clicking four cubes together.
● Show them some pictures of four interlocked cubes and ask them to match their models to the pictures.

HOW TO PLAY

1 Each player places a counter in a different starting position.
2 They roll the dice in turn and move accordingly.
3 They make the shape that they land on using the interlocking cubes.
4 The winner is the first player to make three identical shapes.

NNS FRAMEWORK OBJECTIVES

Game objective
● Make and describe shapes and patterns, for example: explore the different shapes that can be made from four cubes.

Year 5 unit objective
● Visualise 3-D shapes from 2-D drawings.

Links to Unit Plan
Year 5 Spring term
Unit 5a Shape and space

Progression towards the Year 5 objective
● Make a new game board showing shapes made up of 5 interlocking cubes.
● Make a new game board showing 2-D pictures of 3-D shapes – cube, tetrahedron, cone and so on. Players win points by collecting the correct 3-D shape from the box.
● Make a new game board showing the nets of 3-D shapes. Players win points by collecting the correct 3-D shape from the box.

Crazy cubes

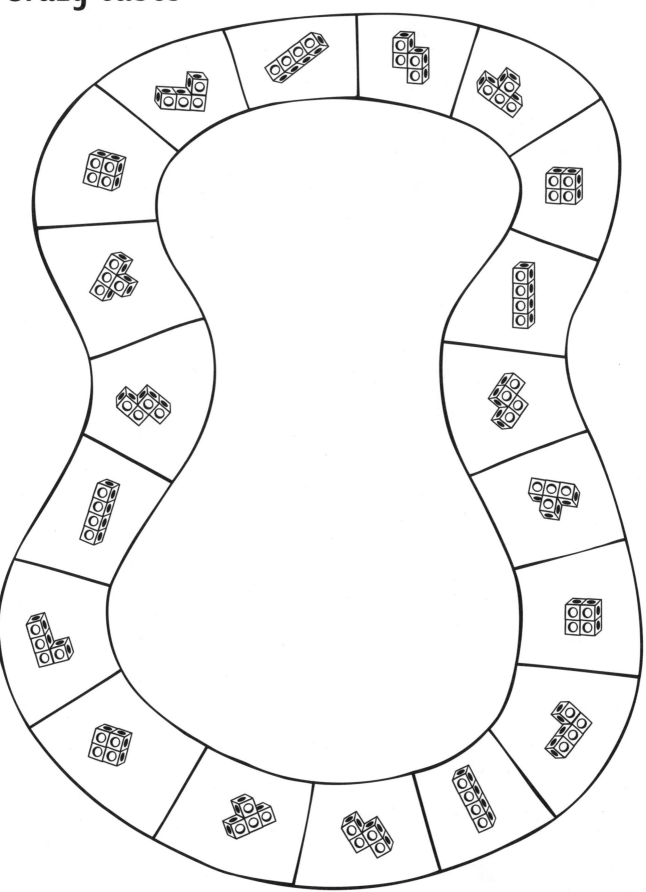

25. What's left?

Grouping
Pairs

Resources
● One dice marked 2, 2, 5, 5, 10, 10
● Counters
● Game board (photocopiable page 71)

● Interactive Teaching Program 'Grouping' (Optional)

Vocabulary
divide
divided by
remainder

Teaching input
Remind the children what is meant by a remainder when dividing and practise some division calculations which involve remainders. Demonstrate how a number line or counters/cubes can be used to help with division.

HOW TO PLAY

1 In turn, players choose a number from the board, roll the dice and divide the chosen board number by the dice number.
2 The board number is then covered by a counter and may not be used again.
3 The score is determined by the remainder:
Example: Player chooses 17 from the board, s/he rolls the dice and scores 5. Remainder when 17 is divided by 5 is 2 – this player scores 2 and 17 is covered with a counter.
4 When all numbers have been covered, the player with the **lowest** score wins.

NNS FRAMEWORK OBJECTIVES

Game objective
● Begin to find remainders after simple division.

Year 5 unit objective
● Begin to express a quotient as a fraction when dividing a whole number by 2, 4, 5 or 10. Round up or down after division, depending on context.

Links to Unit Plan
Year 5 Summer term
Unit 2 Multiplication and division 1

Progression towards the Year 5 objective
● Use a dice marked 2, 3, 4, 5, 10 and blank, and a game board on which some of the numbers have been replaced with larger numbers (the blank face is read as 'miss a turn').
● Change the game board so that the following fractions are shown in random order:
$\frac{1}{2}$ $\frac{1}{4}$ $\frac{3}{4}$ $\frac{1}{5}$ $\frac{2}{5}$ $\frac{3}{5}$ $\frac{4}{5}$ $\frac{1}{5}$ $\frac{3}{10}$ $\frac{7}{10}$ $\frac{9}{10}$ (twice each) and 2 zeros (24 spaces in all).
Each player will need a pile of counters in their preferred colour.

Players then roll two 10 sided dice to generate a two-digit number (a dice roll showing a 3 and a 6 can be used as 36 or 63) and a dice marked 2, 4, 5, 5, 10, 10. Between them, these create numbers for a division (36 ÷ 5, for example).

The players must then cover, with a counter in their colour, the appropriate fractional remainder on the board (in this example, it would be one fifth).

It may be necessary to reduce the remainder to its lowest terms (32 ÷ 4 would give a remainder of $\frac{1}{2}$ not $\frac{2}{4}$, for the purposes of this game).

If the correct fraction cannot be found, the player misses a turn.

When all the fractions have been covered the winner is the player with the most counters on the board.

What's left?

40	26	11	18
14	27	50	28
10	19	25	17
21	24	15	22
13	20	23	12
5	16	29	30

26. Fraction race

Grouping
Groups of 4 children

Resources
Each group of 4 will need:
● One dice marked with
$\frac{1}{2}, \frac{1}{2}, \frac{1}{4}, \frac{1}{5}$, 1, 1
● Four counters (two of each of two different colours)
● Game board (photocopiable page 73)
● A multiplication square
● Interactive Teaching Program 'Fractions' (optional)

Vocabulary
fraction
one whole
one half
one quarter
tenth
eighth
sixth
fifth
equivalent

Teaching input

Discuss with the children what is meant by equivalent fractions.

A set of fraction strips (photocopiable page 74) can be very helpful for those children who are just beginning to develop their understanding of equivalence. Each fraction strip should be cut out separately, but retained as one whole, so that, for example, the halves strip can be placed alongside the tenths strip for direct comparison.

HOW TO PLAY

1 Children play as two teams of two.
2 One team places their two counters on the start positions at one end of the board, while the other team starts from the opposite end of the board.
3 In turn, the teams roll the dice and move either of their two counters to any adjacent hexagon showing a fraction equivalent to the dice score.
4 Example: a dice roll showing $\frac{1}{2}$ would allow a move to a hexagon showing any fraction equivalent to $\frac{1}{2}$.
5 If the team cannot move either of their counters, the turn is missed.
6 The first team to reach the opposite side of the board with both counters wins the game.
Note: In any one turn, players may move only one counter.

NNS FRAMEWORK OBJECTIVES

Game objective
● Begin to recognise simple equivalent fractions: for example, five tenths and one half, five fifths and one whole.

Year 5 objective
● Relate fractions to their decimal representation: that is, recognise the equivalence between the decimal and fraction forms of one half, one quarter, three quarters and tenths and hundredths.

Links to Unit Plan
Year 5 Summer term
Unit 4 Fractions, decimals and percentages

Progression towards the Year 5 objective

● Players play without the help of fraction strips.
● The game board can be amended to show $\frac{1}{2}$, $\frac{1}{4}$, tenths and one whole, with equivalents including their decimal forms.
● Use a more complex game board showing fraction and decimal equivalents of $\frac{1}{2}$, $\frac{1}{4}$, $\frac{3}{4}$, tenths and hundredths. The dice used for this version of the game will need to show 0.1, $\frac{1}{4}$, 0.3, $\frac{1}{2}$, 0.75 and 0.9 (or any combination of the decimal/fraction equivalents of these).
● Any version of the game can be played by two players playing against each other, instead of two teams of two.

Fraction race

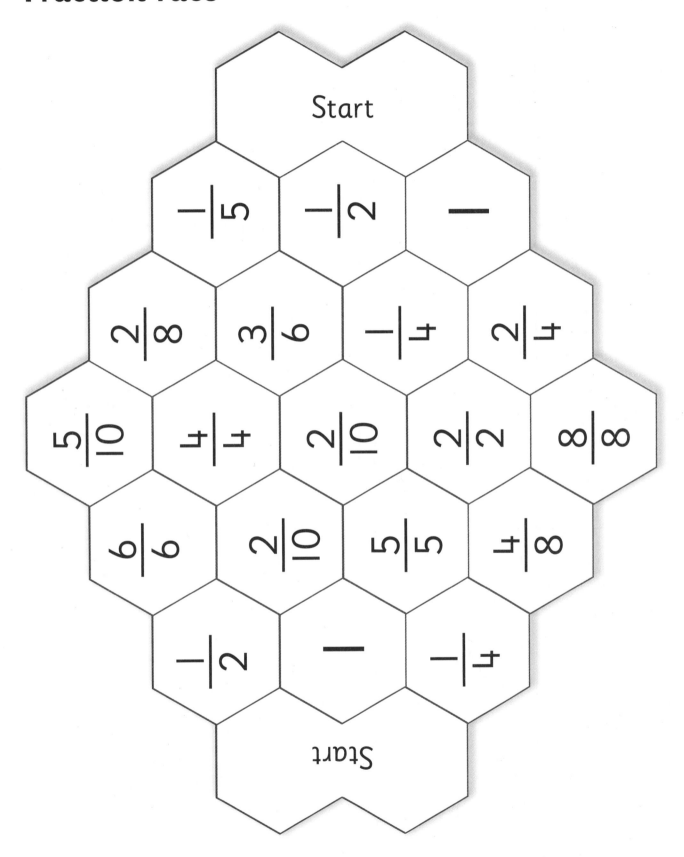

Fraction race (strips)

	$\frac{1}{2}$	$\frac{1}{4}$	$\frac{1}{5}$	$\frac{1}{6}$	$\frac{1}{8}$	$\frac{1}{10}$
			$\frac{1}{5}$	$\frac{1}{6}$	$\frac{1}{8}$	$\frac{1}{10}$
		$\frac{1}{4}$	$\frac{1}{5}$	$\frac{1}{6}$	$\frac{1}{8}$	$\frac{1}{10}$
					$\frac{1}{8}$	$\frac{1}{10}$
	$\frac{1}{2}$	$\frac{1}{4}$	$\frac{1}{5}$	$\frac{1}{6}$	$\frac{1}{8}$	$\frac{1}{10}$
			$\frac{1}{5}$	$\frac{1}{6}$	$\frac{1}{8}$	$\frac{1}{10}$
		$\frac{1}{4}$	$\frac{1}{5}$	$\frac{1}{6}$	$\frac{1}{8}$	$\frac{1}{10}$
				$\frac{1}{6}$	$\frac{1}{8}$	$\frac{1}{10}$

27. What's the time?

Teaching input

Spend a little time practising telling the time on an analogue display and using the appropriate vocabulary. Focus particularly on the difficulties of deciding whether a clock is showing minutes *to* the hour or minutes *past* the hour. When children have had sufficient practice with analogue display, move on to relating the clock face to digital notation. It is helpful to read digital notation such as 9.40, first as 'nine forty' and then as 'twenty minutes to ten'. This helps the children to make the connection between analogue and digital displays.

HOW TO PLAY

1 Shuffle the cards and lay them out face down on the table (a grid arrangement makes the game easier).

2 In turn, the players turn over any two cards.

3 If they match (i.e. they show the same time) the player keeps the cards and has another turn.

4 If they do not match, they are turned face down again and play passes to the next player.

5 The winner is the player with the most cards when they have all been taken.

Grouping
Groups of up to 4 children

Resources
Each group will need:
● A set of time cards (photocopiable pages 76 and 77)
● Rubber stamps of analogue clock faces and digital displays (to assist in the preparation of further time cards/worksheets)
● Interactive Teaching Program 'Tell the Time' (optional)

Vocabulary
hour
minute
o'clock
half past
quarter to
quarter past
digital
analogue
12-hour clock

Progression towards the Year 5 objective

This game can be played in exactly the same way at any level by making a set of cards to match the needs of the players. For example, it could be played with a set of cards showing:

● Analogue time on a 12-hour clock face (showing 23 minutes to 5)
● A card with '23 minutes to 5' written on it
● Digital time using am and pm (4:37pm)
● Digital time using 24-hour notation (16:37).

Players must then find any two matching cards, or all four matching cards, to win that turn.

NNS FRAMEWORK OBJECTIVES

Game objective
● Read the time to five minutes on an analogue clock and a 12-hour digital clock, and use the notation 9:40.

Year 5 unit objective
● Use units of time; read the time on a 24 hour digital clock and use 24-hour clock notation such as 19:53.

Links to Unit Plan
Year 5 Summer term Unit 10 Measures and problem solving

What's the time? (I)

2:25	12:20	9:00
6:10	4:30	11:15
3:45	7:05	5:55
10:40	1:35	8:50

What's the time? (2)

28. Calculating points

Grouping
Pairs

Resources
● One dice marked x10, x10, ÷10, ÷10, x100, Change no.
● 10 cards showing multiples of 10 up to 1000 (selected from photocopiable page 79 to cover a range from 100 to 1000)
● Place value chart (optional)

Vocabulary
multiply
divide
decimal
decimal fraction
decimal point

Teaching input
Discuss with the children the effect of multiplying and dividing numbers by 10 and 100. It is important to stress that when multiplying by 10 each digit in a number is made 10 times bigger and will therefore move one place to the left. For example, when multiplying 25 by 10 the 20 becomes 200 and the 5 becomes 50. This means that the answer must be written as 250 with the zero fixing the position of the 2 and the 5 so that they do, in fact represent 200 and 50 respectively. The reverse happens when dividing by 10.

Many children are wrongly taught to 'add a 0 to the end'. This teaching of course fails them when they begin to work with decimal numbers, since 2.5 x 10 is not 2.50.

HOW TO PLAY
1 Shuffle the multiples of 10 cards and place them face down in a pile.
2 Player 1 takes the top card to give the starting number. The same player then rolls the dice and operates accordingly on the number on the card. This answer is written down.
3 Player 2 uses this new number as the starting number and uses the dice as above.
4 Play continues in this way until one player passes 1000 and thus scores one point.
5 Player 2 takes the top card this time to start the next round.
6 The winner is the player with the most points when all the cards have been used.

Examples:
Card drawn: 250
$250 \div 10 \rightarrow 25$, $\times 100 \rightarrow 2500$ (this player wins a point).
New card: 380
$380 \div 10 \rightarrow 38$, $\div 10$ (this player misses a turn) $\times 10 \rightarrow 380$, $\times 10 \rightarrow 3800$ (this player wins a point).
New card: 140
$140 \div 10 \rightarrow 14$, $\times 10 \rightarrow 140$, change no. $630 \div 10 \rightarrow 63$, $\times 100 \rightarrow 6300$ (this player wins a point).

NNS FRAMEWORK OBJECTIVES

Game objective
● Multiply or divide any integer up to 1000 by 10 (whole number answers), and understand the effect. Begin to multiply by 100.

Year 6 objective
● Multiply and divide decimals by 10 or 100 and integers by 1000, and explain the effect.

Links to Unit Plan
Year 6 Autumn term Unit 1 Place value.

Progression towards the Year 6 objective
● Play as above but (for example) $25 \div 10$ would not be 'miss a turn' but would be calculated as a decimal. A decision would have to be made, depending on the needs and abilities of the children playing the game, whether $2.5 \div 10$ would be 'miss a turn' or not.
● Use three ten-sided dice to generate the start number, and a dice marked x 10, x 100, x 1000, ÷ 10, ÷ 100, change number. The player who returns to the start number in their turn wins the point. For example:
Roll start number 289
$289 \div 10 \rightarrow 28.9$, $\div 10 \rightarrow 2.89$, $\times 100 \rightarrow 289$ (this player wins a point).

Calculating points

110	130	160	170	200
240	280	290	320	350
370	400	410	440	480
520	530	550	590	600
610	620	640	660	690
720	730	750	770	780
810	830	840	850	860
900	910	960	970	980

29. Leftovers

Grouping
Small groups of up to 4 children

Resources
Each group will need:
● One ten-sided dice
● A scoring sheet for each player (photocopiable page 81)
● Interactive Teaching Program 'Grouping' (optional)

Vocabulary
division
divide by
remainder

Teaching input

Before playing the game, the children should have some practice in division. However, the objective of the game is to help children with the recording of division rather than the strategies involved in calculating, so a number line recording of grouping may be more appropriate for some children, rather than the method offered by the work sheet. These children may benefit from using a standard dice to generate their numbers, rather than a ten-sided dice, in order to keep the numbers fairly small.

HOW TO PLAY

1 In turn, players:
● roll the dice three times
● record the numbers
● decide in which positions in the division calculation each number should be placed
● do the calculation and write the answer as quotient and remainder.
2 When all the players in the group have done this the player with the smallest remainder scores a point. (If more than one player gets the same smallest remainder each of them gets a point.)
3 Play continues until all the divisions on the sheet have been completed.
4 The winner is the player with the highest score.

NNS FRAMEWORK OBJECTIVES

Game objectives
● Use informal pencil and paper methods to support, record or explain multiplications and divisions.
● Develop and refine written methods for TU ÷ U.

Year 6 objective
● Use informal pencil and paper methods to support, record or explain multiplications and divisions.

Links to Unit Plan
Year 6 Autumn term Unit 3 Multiplication and division, written methods

Progression towards the Year 6 objective

● Play the game as above but using larger numbers (three-digit numbers divided by single digit numbers or, where appropriate, three-digit by two-digit divisions). Add a box to one or both numbers on the sheet before copying.

Leftovers

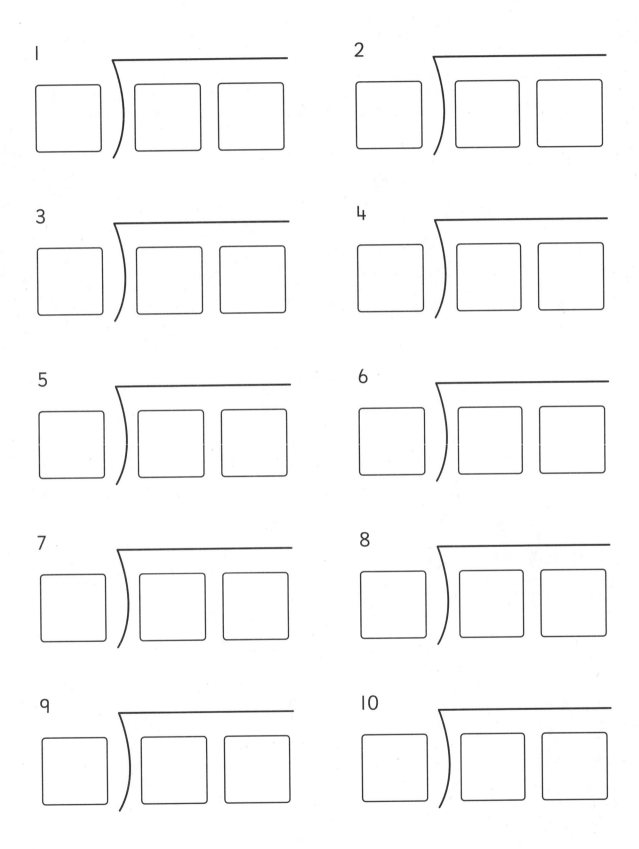

30. Let's co-ordinate

Grouping
Pairs

Resources
● Two ten-sided dice in different colours
● A copy of photocopiable page 83 cut in half to give each player a grid
● Interactive Teaching Program 'Co-ordinates' (optional)

Vocabulary
co-ordinates
horizontal
vertical
straight line
quadrant
square

Teaching input
Remind the children of the correct way to read and find co-ordinates: The first number of the pair is found on the horizontal axis, and the second on the vertical axis. An aid to remembering this might be 'Go in the house before climbing the stairs.' It is important to point out to the children that the co-ordinates (4, 7) do not give the same location as (7,4).

HOW TO PLAY

1 In turn, players roll the two dice together and use the numbers to make a co-ordinate in either order, for example, 4 and 6 can be used to make (4,6) or (6,4).

2 Players mark their co-ordinates on their own grid.

3 The first player to have three co-ordinates which will make a straight line horizontally, vertically or diagonally when joined, wins the game. (The points must be joined using a pencil and ruler to show that they do in fact make a straight line.)

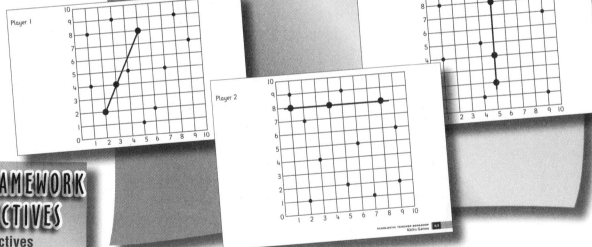

NNS FRAMEWORK OBJECTIVES

Game objectives
● Describe and find the position of a point on a grid of squares where the lines are numbered.
● Recognise simple examples of horizontal and vertical lines.

Year 6 objective
● Read and plot co-ordinates in all four quadrants.

Links to Unit Plan
Year 6 Autumn term
Unit 10 Shape and Space; Position, movement and scales, and solve problems

Progression towards the Year 6 objective

● The game is played as above but the winner is the first player to have four co-ordinates that will make a square when joined.

● Children who are ready to progress beyond the first quadrant can either play in two quadrants or move straight on to using four quadrants.

● To play in two quadrants, use three ten-sided dice, one of which is marked from 0 to negative 9 (−9). This dice represents numbers on the **negative y axis** so that when rolling all three dice together the players can choose two of the three numbers to make a co-ordinate of the form (x, y) or (x, −y).

● To play in all four quadrants, use four ten-sided dice, two of which are marked with negative numbers. Children roll all four together and choose any two of the numbers to make a co-ordinate.

Let's co-ordinate

Player 1

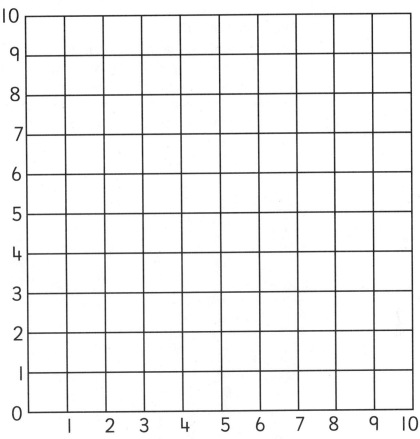

Player 2

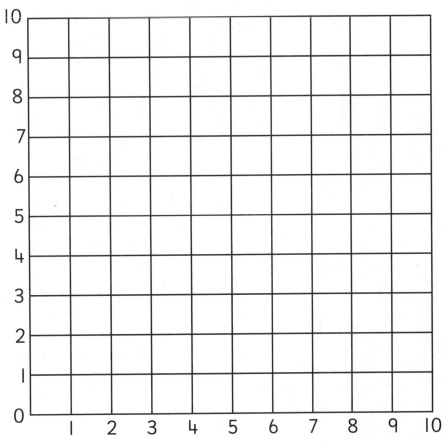

31. To zero and beyond

Teaching input

Using a positive/negative number line or a counting stick, practise with the children moving in positive and negative directions, taking note of the number they start with, the number at which they arrive after the move, and that zero is 'counted' in the move (recognising that it occupies a position on the line). It is important to use the correct vocabulary when referring to negative integers:

–7 is said as 'negative seven' not 'minus seven'.

Grouping
Pairs

Resources
Each pair will need:
● A copy of the game board (photocopiable page 85)
● One ten-sided dice
● One counter to play the game
● A collection of counters (the bank) for scoring
● Interactive Teaching Program 'Number Line' (optional)

Vocabulary
integer
positive
negative
zero

HOW TO PLAY

1 At the start of the game, each player takes 10 scoring counters and the 'game' counter is placed on the start position.

2 In turn players roll the dice and move the counter that number of places in a positive or negative direction (the player who rolled the dice chooses the direction of the move).

3 If the counter lands on a positive number, the player collects that number of scoring counters from the bank. If the counter lands on a negative number s/he must give the bank that number of scoring counters from his/her own collection.

4 A player may not move in such a way as to take the counter off the board.

5 The first player to have 30 or more counters wins the game. For example: player 1 rolls a 5 and chooses to move 5 in a positive direction, landing on the number 5, and collects 5 counters (now has total of 15). Player 2 rolls a 7 so may not move in a positive direction (12 is off the board). S/he moves 7 in a negative direction, landing on –2, and must give the bank 2 counters (now has a total of 8).

6 The game continues in this way until the winner is decided.

NNS FRAMEWORK OBJECTIVES

Game objective
● Recognise negative numbers in context (e.g. on a number line, on a temperature scale).

Year 6 objective
● Find the difference between a positive and negative integer, or two negative integers, in the context such as temperature or a number line, and order a set of positive and negative integers.

Links to Unit Plan
Year 6 Spring term
Unit 1 Place value

Progression towards the Year 6 objective

● The game can be played in a similar way but without the use of a number line. In this case the score would be calculated and recorded using pencil and paper. The numbers must stay within the range –10 to 10. Each player would keep an independent score. For example:

1   Both players begin with zero on their score sheet.

2   Player 1 rolls 2, cumulative score 2.

3   Player 2 rolls 2, cumulative score 2.

4   Player 1 rolls 9, cannot add 9 as this would be outside the permitted range (2 + 9 = 11), so must subtract 9. Cumulative score (2 – 9) is –7.

5   Player 2 rolls 3, cumulative score (2 + 3) is 5.

6   Player 2 wins this round as 5 is greater than –7.

*Note: A 'round' consists of **two** dice rolls for each player.*

To zero and beyond

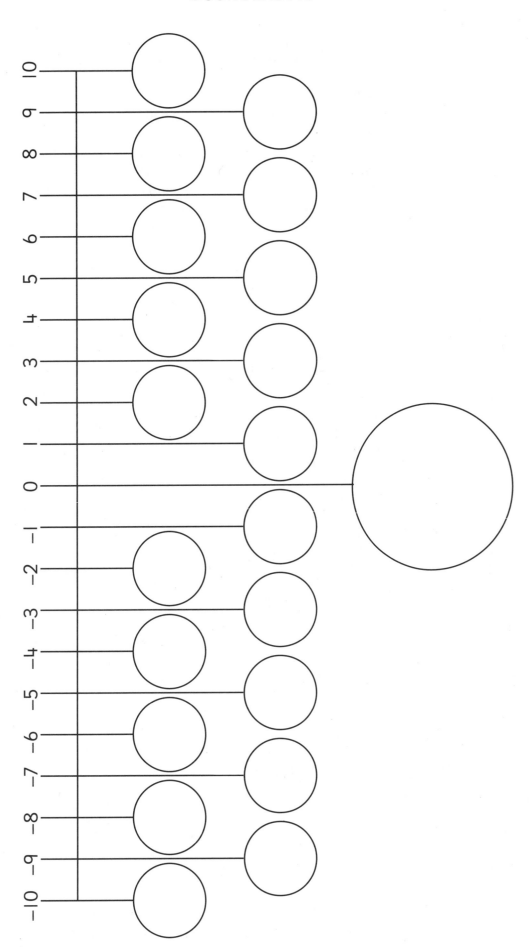

32. Decimal dominoes

Grouping
Small groups of up to 4 children

Resources
Each group will need:
● One set of double six dominoes with the double blank removed
● Recording sheet (photocopiable page 87) and rough paper for each player
● A calculator for checking

Vocabulary
place value
tenth
hundredth
decimal
decimal point

Teaching input

In preparation for the game explain and demonstrate the use of dominoes to represent decimal numbers. Children may need to revise decimal notation and be reminded of place value in decimal numbers. They may also need reinforcement of the fact that _hundredths_ are smaller than _tenths_, as they may confuse the words with _hundreds_ (larger) and _tens_ (smaller). It may be necessary to use, for example, base 10 materials or squared paper to show clearly the difference and relationship between hundredths and tenths.

HOW TO PLAY

1 Spread out the dominoes face down on the table.
2 Each player takes two dominoes from the set and turns them face up.
3 Each player must consider what each of their dominoes could represent and write down all the possibilities. For example: the (5, 2) domino could represent 0.52, 0.25, 5.2 or 2.5 and the (0, 4) domino could represent 0.04, 0.4 or 4.0.
4 Each player then chooses the smallest number (0.04) and the largest number (5.2) from this list and adds them together/finds the difference. Other players check using a calculator.
5 The player with the largest/smallest total/difference wins the game.
    Note: The targets to win can be changed to suit the needs and abilities of the children (for example, the player with the total/difference nearest to a given number wins the game).

Game objective
● Understand decimal notation and place value for tenths and hundredths, and use it in context.

Year 6 objective
● Use known number facts and place value to consolidate mental addition/subtraction.

Links to Unit Plan
Year 6 Spring term
Unit 7 Addition and subtraction

Progression towards the Year 6 objective

There are several modifications which can be made to this game:
● Use a double 9 set of dominoes with the double blank removed.
● Players select three or more dominoes from the set in each round of the game and list, then order, all the possible numbers before operating upon them.
● Players must total all the possible numbers, the largest/smallest total winning the game (this may require written calculations rather than mental and players can check each other's calculations with a calculator).

Decimal dominoes

My dominoes are:

My largest number is:

My smallest number is:

The difference is:

The total is:

My dominoes are:

My largest number is:

My smallest number is:

The difference is:

The total is:

My dominoes are:

My largest number is:

My smallest number is:

The difference is:

The total is:

My dominoes are:

My largest number is:

My smallest number is:

The difference is:

The total is:

My dominoes are:

My largest number is:

My smallest number is:

The difference is:

The total is:

My dominoes are:

My largest number is:

My smallest number is:

The difference is:

The total is:

My dominoes are:

My largest number is:

My smallest number is:

The difference is:

The total is:

33. Measure for measure

Grouping
Pairs

Resources
● A set of cards (made from photocopiable page 89)

Vocabulary
kilometres
metres
centimetres
millimetres
kilograms
grams
litres
centilitres
millilitres

Teaching input
Revise with the children the correct vocabulary and notation for length and capacity. Focus particularly on the relationships between litres, centilitres and millilitres and between kilometres, metres, centimetres and millimetres. Remind children that there are different ways for expressing the same measurement, for example: 50cm can also be written as 0.5m, ½m or 500mm.

HOW TO PLAY
1 Spread out all the cards face down on the table.
2 In turn players choose two cards and turn them over.
3 If the cards match the player keeps both cards.
4 If they don't match, they are returned face down to their original position.
5 The winner is the player with more cards when they have all been used.

NNS FRAMEWORK OBJECTIVES

Game objectives
● Use, read and write standard metric units (km, m, cm, mm, kg, g, l, ml), including their abbreviations.
● Know and use the relationships between familiar units of length, mass and capacity.

Year 6 objective
● Use, read and write standard metric units of length, mass and capacity (km, m, cm, mm, kg, g, l, ml, cl), including their abbreviations, and relationships between them.

Links to Unit Plan
Year 6 Spring term
Unit 9 Measures and problem solving

Progression towards the Year 6 objective
● Include cards which show centilitres.
● Include cards which show the decimal representations of the measures (for example 0.9m and 90cm, 3.286kg and 3286g and so on).
● Play snap rather than matching pairs.
● Play 'War Games' with a similar set of cards but representing length, mass or capacity **only**, and showing various styles of representation.
(2460g, 3.56kg, 1kg – 423g and so on):
1 Cards are placed face down in a pile.
2 Players each draw one card and reveal them.
3 The player whose card represents a greater quantity keeps both cards (if they are the same players keep one card each).
4 The winner is the player with more cards when they have all been used.

Measure for measure

3km	700cm	3cm	4kg
3000m	7m	30mm	4000g
5m	4000cm	2kg	4000ml
5000mm	40m	2000g	4l
1km	8000ml	4cm	600cm
1000m	8l	40mm	6m

34. Money in its place

Grouping
Pairs

Resources
Each pair of children will need:
● Game board (photocopiable page 91)
Note: The main game uses the top number line, with each of the other number lines used (in order) for one of the variations. Cut up several copies of the sheet to provide each group with a suitable level number line
● Three standard dice, one in one colour (eg red), two in another colour (eg blue)
● Pencils or felt pens in two different colours

Vocabulary
pounds
pennies
more than
less than
the same as
between
tenth
hundredth
decimal
decimal point

Teaching input

Discuss and revise with the children decimal notation for money. Give particular attention to the decimal notation for amounts of money in certain cases:

● **The number 4½ represented as a decimal fraction is 4.5 (no zero) whereas £4.50 does have a zero (particularly relevant when using a calculator for money calculations – the answer to £5.27 – 77p would appear in the display as 4.5).**

● **The notation £4.05 represents four pounds and five pence (not fifty pence).**

HOW TO PLAY

1 Both players play on **one** of the number lines.

2 In turn players roll the three dice together. The (red) dice determines how many pounds in the amount of money, the two (blue) ones determine how many pennies. (For example a throw of 5 (red), 3 (blue) and 6 (blue) could be £5.36 or £5.63 – the player decides.)

3 Players mark the position of this amount of money on their own number line using a pencil or felt pen in the chosen colour, looking carefully at any amounts that may have been written on the line already.

4 The winner is the player who gets three amounts of money in a line with none of the other player's amounts between them.

NNS FRAMEWORK OBJECTIVES

Game objective
● Understand decimal notation and place value for tenths and hundredths and use it in context, for example, order amounts of money.

Year 6 objective
● Order a mixed set of numbers with up to three decimal places.

Links to Unit Plan
Year 6 Summer term Unit 1, Decimals, fractions, percentages

Progression towards the Year 6 objective

● Use three ten-sided dice and a blank table-top number line 0–10 for counting in ones, with the positions equivalent to whole pounds marked. This allows ordering of amounts of money from zero to £9.99.

● Use the blank table-top 0–10 number line with the positions marked only with 1, 2, 3… so that the game becomes one of ordering decimal numbers rather than money.

● Use the blank table-top 0–10 number line with the positions unmarked. Players roll two ten sided dice only, divide the smaller number by the larger (using a calculator) to create a decimal number, and using only the first three digits after the decimal point (where there are more), locate the number on the number line.

Money in its place

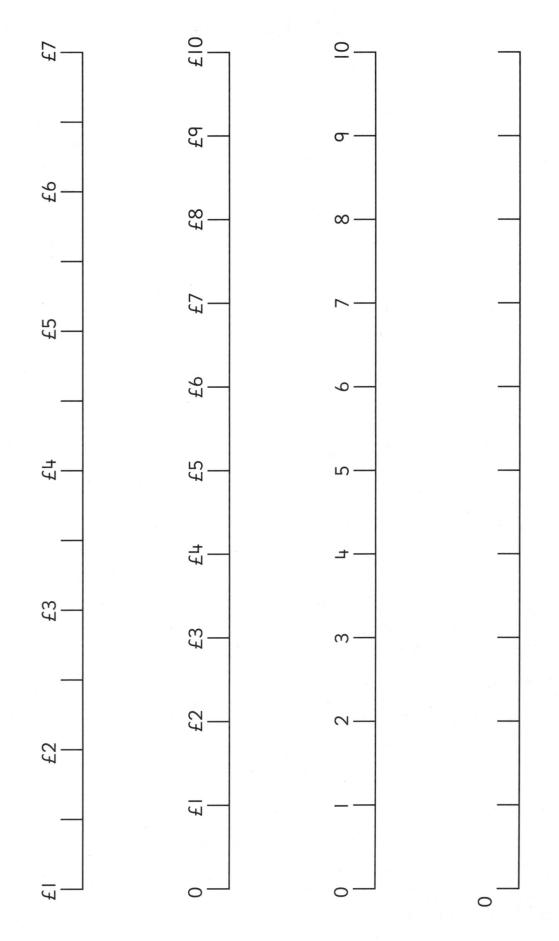

35. Exactly right

Grouping
Pairs

Resources
● Game board (photocopiable page 93)
● Two ten-sided dice in different colours
● Crayons or coloured pencils in two colours
● A calculator

Vocabulary
divide into
remainder

Teaching input

In preparation for the game, children should practise the tables they are going to use. It is important that they do not simply 'chant' the tables in order (a useful warm-up to other tables activities) but should also be able to recall individual facts from any table they are familiar with on demand.

HOW TO PLAY

1 Players decide which dice will represent tens and which will represent units.

2 In turn they roll both dice together to generate a two digit number.

3 They colour any one number on the game board which will divide exactly into it, in their own colour (the other player may use a calculator to check).

4 The first player to colour three numbers in a row, horizontally, vertically or diagonally, is the winner.

NNS FRAMEWORK OBJECTIVES

Game objective
● Derive quickly division facts corresponding to 2, 3, 4, 5 and 10 times-tables.

Year 6 objective
● Derive quickly division facts corresponding to tables up to 10 x 10.

Links to Unit Plan
Year 6 Summer term
Unit 2 Calculations

Progression towards the Year 6 objective

● Gradually introduce 6, 7, 8 and 9 to the board according to which tables facts the children are familiar with. Increase the size of the board accordingly and play 'four in a row' rather than 'three in a row'.

Exactly right

36. Lines and angles

Teaching input

Using a set of 2-D shapes, remind the children of the correct names for shapes and discuss their properties. Focus particularly on the fact that some shapes are totally defined by their name (for example, a square) but that some names can be interpreted differently (for example, a trapezium can be right angled or isosceles but must have exactly one pair of parallel sides).

Refresh children's knowledge of the properties of triangles, parallel lines (including the fact that they can be parallel without being equal and vice versa) and lines of symmetry.

HOW TO PLAY

1 Shuffle the cards and place them face down in a pile.
2 In turn, players take the top card and consider its properties.
3 On their own score sheet they place a tick in each column that is correct for their shape (for example, a right angled isosceles triangle would have a tick in the first, third and sixth columns).
4 The total number of ticks for that shape is recorded in the final column.
5 When all the cards have been used the winner is the player with the greater total score.

Progression towards the Year 6 objective

Make a new score card showing more complex properties according to the needs and abilities of the children. For example (**not** an exhaustive list):
● Exactly one pair of parallel sides
● Exactly two lines of symmetry
● No sides equal
● Opposite sides equal
● Opposite sides equal and parallel
● Diagonals equal in length
● Diagonals intersect at right angles.

Lines and angles

One right angle	At least two right angles	One line of symmetry	At least two lines of symmetry	At least one pair of parallel sides	At least two equal sides	Score
					Total	

Shapes

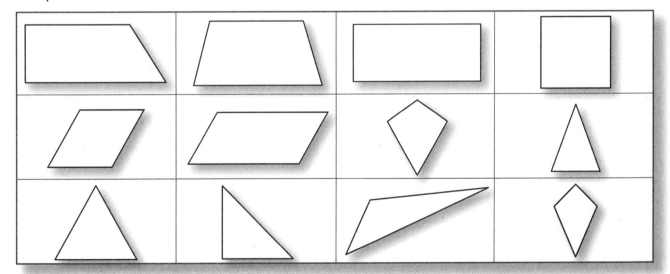

Feedback/recording sheet

Game name and number _____

Date played _____

Which children were able to play this game successfully?

Which children needed significant help?

Did any children find the game too difficult to manage?

List any aspects of the mathematics and/or vocabulary that you feel need additional teaching/consolidation:

Name any child/children who you think did exceptionally well, and identify how: